LY

The author was born in Africa and educated there and in Britain, taking his doctorate in animal behaviour under the supervision of Desmond Morris at London Zoo.

He has been involved in anthropology in Indonesia and Brazil, archaeology in Jordan and Peru, palaeontology in South and East Africa, and marine biology in the Indian Ocean – representing Seychelles on the International Whaling Commission.

For the past fifteen years, he has been pursuing the paranormal, travelling constantly from his base in the far west of Ireland, pausing only to publish his bestsellers SUPERNATURE, THE BIOLOGY OF DEATH (formerly entitled THE ROMEO ERROR), GIFTS OF UNKNOWN THINGS, LIFE-TIDE and HEAVEN'S BREATH.

Lyall Watson's recent books include WHALES OF THE WORLD, DREAMS OF DRAGONS (published in hardback as EARTHWORKS) and SUPER-NATURE II (published in hardback as BEYOND SUPERNATURE). He is working on THE SECRET LIFE OF MACHINES and a biography of Raymond Dart, the discoverer of the first African apeman.

Lyall Watson

NEOPHILIA
The Tradition of the New

First published in Great Britain in
1989 as a Sceptre paperback
original.

Sceptre is an imprint of Hodder and
Stoughton Paperbacks, a division of
Hodder and Stoughton Ltd.

British Library C.I.P.

Watson, Lyall.
  Neophilia: the tradition of the
new.
  1. Innovation
  I. Title
  303.4'84

  ISBN 0-340-49481-6

Printed and bound in Great Britain
for Hodder and Stoughton Paper-
backs, a division of Hodder and
Stoughton Ltd., Mill Road, Dunton
Green, Sevenoaks, Kent TN13 2YA
(Editorial Office: 47 Bedford
Square, London WC1B 3DP) by
Richard Clay Ltd., Bungay, Suffolk.
Photoset by Rowland Photo-
typesetting Ltd., Bury St Edmunds,
Suffolk.

'We have learned so well how to absorb novelty that receptivity itself has turned into a kind of tradition – "the tradition of the new".'

Richard Hofstadter

CONTENTS

INTRODUCTION

はじめに

INTRODUCTION

There is an enormous difference between lions and tigers.

Physically, there is little to separate them. It takes an expert anatomist to distinguish between the two great cats without their skins. But psychologically, they are worlds apart.

Lions, by nature, are idle beasts. Provided they have enough to eat, they can easily accept a lazy way of life, happily dozing their days away in the shade of a convenient tree. Tigers are much more demanding. They have nervous systems that object to inactivity and make it impossible for them to relax for very long, no matter how well fed they may be. Which is why tigers are that much more difficult to keep in captivity, where they tend to become bored and listless and take to pacing up and down.

As a zoo director, I came very quickly to recognise this distinction. I learned to divide all my charges into two basic types – the specialists and the opportunists. In the first group are those, like the lion, who adapt well to being taken from the wild. And in the second are those, like the tiger, who never stop exploring and investigating and need to keep constantly on the move. Lions, eagles, snakes and anteaters are easy to please. Give them the food they like and a warm place to sleep and they thrive in a zoo, often producing embarrassing numbers of offspring. But tigers, wolves, monkeys and apes are difficult and temperamental and need very special care if they are not to become neurotic.

Most animal species fall into the lion category. They are inherently conservative, seeking out the old and the usual, the comfortable things. There are some human individuals, even a few entire cultures, that are like this. But as a species, we tend to be tigers. We enjoy a challenge. We actively pursue the new and different. We like being pushed and stretched. We look for excitement and deliberately put ourselves at risk. We are, in a simple and rather useful word, *neophilic* – 'fond of that which is new'.

The *neophobic* species – 'those which hate the new' – tend to be specialists which have evolved one particular survival trick to the exclusion of all others, a pattern which rules their lives. Anteaters, for instance, are extraordinarily good at finding and eating ants. Their whole anatomy and behaviour is modified to make them better at this activity than anyone else around. Nobody can devour quite so many ants in such a short space of time. Which is fine as long as the ants last, but if anything were to happen to this single source of food, anteaters would very quickly follow the ants into antiquity. There is no future for a specialist who cannot practise his or her speciality.

Neophilic species, on the other hand, are determined non-specialists. They never stop exploring and investigating and are always on the lookout for something in the environment that can be bent to their advantage. They are constantly on the go, ready to exploit whatever it is that happens, able to bend and adapt to the times. This, in essence, is the secret of human success. We are the supreme opportunists. Not particularly good at anything, except being willing to try anything at all. We cannot climb very high, run very fast, dive very deep or leap great buildings at a single bound. But we do most of these things reasonably well and remain able to turn our bodies, and our minds, to doing whatever is necessary, not only to survive, but to thrive.

I learned about zoos thirty years ago as a student of Desmond Morris at London Zoo. It was there that he first compared zoos to modern cities, pointing out that the denizens of both suffered from the artificiality of their respective situations. The city, he said, is not so much a concrete jungle as a human zoo in which the inhabitants, being basically neophilic, react to their unpleasant circumstances with remarkable ingenuity. Removed from our natural habitat, where we once lived as members of a tribe in a rich and challenging environment, we find cities fundamentally dull. They fail to satisfy our need for constant stimulus and so we set about rectifying their shortcomings in a number of fascinating ways.

We create unnecessary problems, inventing labour-wasting devices to help fill the time between the cradle and the grave. Our basic needs are taken care of by society, so we make difficulties for ourselves. We allow our jobs to become more complex than necessary. We fill our leisure time with more and more elaborate recreations. We tempt fate by courting danger, taking risks and deliberately making manoeuvres that are likely to leave us fighting for our physical or social lives. Sometimes, in more rational moments, we tempt survival by proxy, encouraging others into taking risks on our behalf, betting on their success. Or we just sit back and identify with the thrills of seduction and murder as they affect the lives of fictional characters in books and films.

We look, in our own lives, for more complex forms of expression, experimenting with arts and sciences that give free rein to our gigantic brains. We write and perform symphonies and plays, we look at paintings, listen to operas and train our bodies to athletic perfection for gymnastics and ballet. We exaggerate for added effect, breeding bigger and brighter flowers, cooking spicier foods, wearing stronger perfumes and more eye-catching clothing. We accentuate our characters with cosmetics, dramatising hairy chests, smooth legs and rosy lips. We go to extremes in cartoon and caricature, making points by magnifying particular features, manipulating stimulus and response by distorting reality in carefully selected ways. Making sure, always, that we wring the last drops of stimulation out of every source of variation in our cages.

All this is healthy and exciting, but it is pointless to pretend that everything in the human zoo is lovely or can be made rewarding. We face also the dangers of overreacting – in the manner of the female elephant that, in just one typical zoo day, devoured 1706 peanuts, 1320 sweets, 1089 pieces of bread, 811 biscuits, 198 segments of orange, 17 apples, 16 pieces of paper, 7 ice creams, a hamburger, a bootlace and a lady's white leather glove. She wasn't hungry. She had access to a balanced diet, but this didn't include a normal ration of social interaction. So she sought the solace and the contact she needed in another species and, in order to keep their attention, was forced to accept the thoughtless offerings of food from human passers-by.

Because our early environment demanded intense and active exploration, we remain subject to all the risks of behavioural overflow. The need for a rapid response no longer exists, but we go on anyway, sometimes doing stupid and inappropriate things, simply because action, any action at all, is better than doing nothing. As a consequence, we end up abusing ourselves, smashing things or attacking other people without rhyme or reason – and suffer, as a result, all the symptoms of stress. Some of these we relieve with chemicals, or by doing exercises that cut down on stimulation or inhibit our more manic response. Others we simply have to learn to live with.

Neophilia is not without its problems, but it is, on balance, a positive and powerful force in human evolution. Without it, we could be primate lions, content to lie down in some paleolithic pasture, happy with our ability to steal a march on less inventive apes by killing and eating the occasional rabbit. With it, we have blazed a trail through early carnivory to an omnivorous attitude that makes it possible for us to eat or think or do almost anything.

This book is a celebration of neophilia – of our curiosity for, and our fascination with, everything that is new and strange and rare.

This is what being human is all about.

Lyall Watson, Ph.D.
Ballydehob, Eire, 1988

1

宇宙のためいき

ONE

IN THE BEGINNING

You can still hear the Big Bang.

The cosmos is bathed in background noise. There is a constant sort of dismal universal hiss, like static on a radio, that reverberates round and about out little world. Microwave receivers put into high-flying planes, or on to orbiting satellites above our everyday din, can pick it up quite clearly. Measurements made in this way suggest that these echoes can be traced back to their original source, back to an immense explosion which took place 15,000 million years ago.

The oddest feature of these echoes is that they are extraordinarily uniform, as though the explosion occurred simultaneously everywhere, filling all of space from the very beginning. There is a slight decrease in the level of noise in the direction of the constellation of Aquarius, and an equivalent increase in the opposite area occupied by Leo. This tells us that our particular galaxy is travelling towards the constellation Leo at about 1.3 million miles an hour, but the bias is very slight and doesn't interfere with the general conclusion that the universe as a whole is expanding as a result of that distant and cataclysmic event.

Steven Weinberg, the Nobel prize-winning physicist at Harvard, has written a fascinating scenario for the origins of the cosmos. Things began, he suggests, with a sudden rise in temperature that brought all matter to a heat of 100,000 million degrees Centigrade. Such a temperature was, of course, too hot for particles to have any stable existence at all. They were annihilated as fast as they were formed. This inconceivable storm continued for just three minutes, going on until the temperature dropped to a mere 1,000 million degrees, cool enough for nuclei of hydrogen and helium to begin to have an independent existence. Which was the beginning of all concrete matter, though it took another 700,000 years before such nuclei had slowed down sufficiently to be able to join with stray electrons to produce the first actual atoms of gas. It was not until millions of years later that these atoms clumped together under the influence of gravity, condensing ultimately into our existing galaxies.

In his bestselling book of the same title, Weinberg presents a convincing case for this account of the First Three Minutes. It gives us an elegant overview of a finely orchestrated event which helps us to understand that the Big Bang was an immense, but surprisingly gentle, explosion – not so much a blow-out as a steady and organised inflation which continues still. However, even Weinberg admits that the title of his book was misleading. His story begins only one-hundredth of a second after the moment of creation, picking up at a point where the universe is already extremely hot and about the size of a football. For it is only at that point that the rules of general relativity come into play.

Einstein's equations work well when applied to any observable phenomenon and can be used to explain and predict the behaviour of macroscopic events, but are powerless to account for the changes that must have taken place during the first crucial one-hundredth of a second. It was during this time that the football of super-dense, extraordinarily warm cosmic stuff was created out of nothing, blown up from a seed derived from nowhere.

This gap in our knowledge, short as it is, remains immense in its implications. It is large enough to hold any philosophy you like. The fact that general physics can only wind the universe back to a zero point represented by that hot dense football, leaves room for metaphysical speculation and for arguments about a first cause. It is possible, suggests the Head of the Vatican Observatory – a respected astronomer who happens also to be a Jesuit – that this is where the Creator comes in. Maybe it took Him only one-hundredth of a second, rather than the traditional six days, to create the world as we now know it. Perhaps, in the beginning, there really was a God.

It doesn't matter whether you call this vital impulse God or Atman or any of the many names given to the heroes of creation myths. The impulse lives and works in that crucial and mysterious one-hundredth of a second, and continues to be an embarrassment to scientists who find it difficult to reconcile fact and faith. But there may be help at hand.

Even those physicists who worry about such things agree that there must once have been what they call a *singularity* – a moment when time actually began, when the universe was compressed into a mathematical point, something of zero volume and infinite density. And they agree too that any description of this moment and its conditions will be possible only with the help of quantum mechanics and someone with a very special mind. Someone, perhaps, like Stephen Hawking of Cambridge University.

Hawking is a phenomenon. He is a mathematician and a physicist with the ability to think along truly unusual lines and to communicate what he finds in simple equations and lucid prose. He has used the strange logic of quantum physics, and its ability to deal with uncertainty, to produce a new and exciting model of how the universe works.

Imagine, Hawking says, the surface of a sphere like our own globe. Draw the tiniest possible circle around the North Pole to represent the entire universe, in both space and time, at the end of the first one-hundredth of a second. Inside this circle, at its mathematical centre, lies the singularity that marks the moment of creation. Outside it, like lines of latitude, you can draw any number of larger circles representing the progressive expansion of the universe during the last 15,000 million years. Each circle will be larger than the one before, until you reach the equator. Then something interesting happens. Even though succeeding circles are drawn further away from the singularity at the North Pole, more distant from it in time, they will become progressively smaller. The universe, in effect, will begin to shrink rather than expand, and it will continue doing so until it reaches another singularity, another mathematical point, at the South Pole.

Now, Hawking continues, comes the difficult but crucial point. Imagine that there is no difference between the two Poles on this globe. North and South are the same. The universe expands until it reaches its biggest size and then reverses itself, contracting into the *same* singularity. The universe has a beginning and an end, but they are the same. It has no edge and no boundaries to time or space. It is continuous and, to a very real extent, alive in the sense that it seems to be breathing in and out and keeps on bouncing back.

This concept of the cosmos as an organic system is a vital one. It reduces the famous Big Bang, for all its echoes, to nothing more than a label stuck on the surface of Hawking's sphere – just one point in an ongoing life-cycle that we pass through again and again, like a pause for thought between one breath and the next.

There is a certain comfort to be derived from such far-reaching models, which allow the known laws of physics to operate in accordance with the observed behaviour of the universe. Hawking has succeeded brilliantly in tying the whole thing together with two basic sets of equations representing gravity and matter. However, I have a feeling that the problem of creation doesn't end there.

I take some solace from the thought that we live, as it were, in a stream of vibrant exhalation. But can't help wondering what it was, in the first place, that led to such a long and heartfelt sigh.

'Sighs,' according to the English poet Thomas Shadwell, 'are the natural language of the heart.'

But whose?

2
地球が生まれた日
_{ガイア}

TWO

THE WHOLE EARTH

Strictly speaking, there is nothing new in the universe.

As I take a long breath before beginning to write, I am conscious of the fact that the half litre of air I borrow contains millions of molecules once inhaled by both Confucius and Copernicus – who, in turn, mixed their lungfuls with those of the first amphibian to haul itself up on to dry land at the end of the Devonian.

We are locked into a pattern of energy use which is governed by the three great Laws of Thermodynamics. These are usually defined in complex terms, but they can be paraphrased as:

> You can't win;
> You must lose;
> And there's no way out of the game.

Scientists fuss about the form and meaning of the Laws, but their effects are well established in folklore and aptly described, by most cultures on Earth, in variations of the common catchphrases:

> You can't get something for nothing;
> It does no good to cry over spilt milk;
> And you'll never beat the system.

Yet the very existence of life on Earth stands in direct contradiction to such sentiment or science. Life manages to bend the rules without spoiling the game. It hedges all bets, creating order out of disorder, making sense of a system that has an inherent tendency towards nonsense, sliding off, if left to its own devices, into confusion and chaos.

I will look at life, in my usual sidelong way, in the next chapter. But before doing so, I need to consider the only place we can be certain that it exists – right here on Earth.

There is something odd about Earth. To be precise, almost everything about our world is peculiar. It is a cosmic misfit, a planet which breaks all the rules.

According to the Laws of Thermodynamics, Earth ought by now to have reached equilibrium. Five thousand million years should have been quite long enough to turn our hot young world into a tired old one on which everything has slid into a state of inert uniformity.

Scientific logic leads to the prediction that a world as old as ours must necessarily be lifeless, covered in all probability with nothing more than a thin layer of very salty water, kept constantly near boiling point under an atmosphere of almost solid carbon dioxide. By rights, and every reasonable law of nature, our planet ought to be dead.

But it isn't, of course. As I write and you read this, Earth positively hums with vibrant life. The ocean is not nearly as salty as it ought to be by now, succeeding instead in mixing its constituents and returning excess salt to the land in ways which we still only dimly comprehend. The atmosphere remains rich in oxygen and nitrogen, somehow keeping these volatile gases uncombined and up there in the air, like a juggler defying the laws of chemistry. The winds blow and, against all the odds, life blossoms.

Order grows out of anarchy – and none of this makes sense. Nevertheless, it wasn't until 1969 that anyone stood up and said, 'Look here! This is all very well, but there's something funny going on.' The whistle-blower was a British scientist – perhaps the last of a defiant breed of independent thinkers. Such people used to be more common and still go their own way, refusing to be tied to the system, working alone with minimal resources and without elaborate equipment, but succeeding nevertheless – in large part because of their circumstances – in challenging accepted belief.

James Lovelock suggested in 1969 that the stability of our atmosphere, whose composition and temperature remain remarkably stable, can only be explained by assuming that it is linked somehow with the biosphere – tied to the sum total of all living things on the planet. Lovelock said, in effect, that our blanket of air stays where it is, keeping conditions just right for life, because life makes it that way, and requires that it go on doing so. He locked this reciprocal relationship into an elegant ecological cycle by proposing that the lithosphere (the inorganic substance of earth itself) combines with the atmosphere and the biosphere to form an integrated system; the body, as it were, of a single gigantic organism. One self-sustaining creature. The largest living thing in the solar system.

Lovelock named this great organism after the ancient Greek Earth goddess – Gaia. And in the generation since he did so, she has come vividly to life and into consciousness.

One can almost give her date of birth. Gaia was conceived in the mists of solar evolution and christened at Princeton in 1969, but she came to life and mind, taking on her proper weight, on that momentous day in 1966 when, like a monkey with a mirror, we saw ourselves for the first time in those shattering photographs of the Whole Earth.

I will never forget the moment. I knew, as most of us did intellectually, that the Earth was round. We had all been prepared, by the first satellite pictures with their softly curved horizons, to see larger arcs of the planet's circumference. But nothing paved the way for the shock of that first view of our body in its entirety. Nothing could have prepared us for the sight of that wispy, white-capped sapphire, so different from its lifeless neighbours, floating so serenely, so delicately and defiantly, through the wastes of space. It was a sight that stopped millions of us in our tracks, hammering home something that we had known for a long time, but never truly admitted to ourselves.

Something happened on that day, something synaptic, adding

emotion to intellect, reaching critical mass, linking us together as never before, making all mankind a conscious part of the Gaian nervous system. Giving the world a conscience as well as consciousness.

That was the day that Earth became self-aware.

The change was a vital one, in many ways not unlike that which takes place during the early development of every human brain. Starting about seven weeks after conception, the brain of each embryo is rocked by a population explosion. Growth up to that point has been slow and steady, but suddenly it spirals. The number of cells begins to increase by many millions every day, blossoming in the next five weeks to reach the brain's natural limit of 10,000 million. Then the multiplication ends, just as suddenly as it began, making way for a different kind of development. For the rest of pregnancy, and on into the first five years of independent life, the cells in the brain reach out to make contact with each other. Some of them forging as many as a quarter of a million microscopic links with their nearest neighbours, knitting the grey matter into an awesome tangle.

Human life has multiplied in much the same way. There were perhaps 20 million of us around at the time of the Neolithic Revolution. It took 10,000 years to double that number, then 5,000 more to double that – the intervals gradually growing shorter until the population of Earth reached 1,000 million in about 1840. We hit the 2,000 million mark in 1930, 4,000 million in 1976 and – according to the best recent estimates – are likely only to stabilise at around 10,000 million (the same magic number) somewhere near the year 2095.

Meanwhile, the process of interconnection has begun. In 1976, there were only 200 million isolated telephones in the world, a communication network no more complex than that which exists in a region of the human brain the size of a child's fingernail. Today, just over a decade later, there are ten times that number of instruments, all directly connected to each other and to the vast bank of information stored in the world's computers. Our data-processing capacity doubles every year or two and it will not be long before the global network rivals the human brain in complexity, becoming a sort of artificial, but nevertheless planetary, intelligence.

Our world already crackles with electronic conversation and the endless chatter of computers exchanging information. No intergalactic probe coming close enough to us to pick up the echoes would be left in any doubt about our vital signs. This planet is alive and well and getting restless, beginning to seem more and more like an organism – one with a real interest in its surroundings.

Or, to look at it in another way, like a nerve cell in a growing brain, putting out tentative fibres, searching for others similarly occupied.

And that is a thought new and bright enough to keep even a neophilic mind busy for a while.

3

生命の兆候

THREE

SIGNS OF LIFE

Is there a connection between God and golf?

Arguments in science about the origin of life and the question of design, turn surprisingly often to metaphors drawn from golf. Such comparisons tell us something, perhaps, about the relative affluence of the scientists involved, but are actually more revealing about the nature of the game.

Golf, more than any other popular sport, involves a strong random element. Tennis balls and footballs can take unpredictable trajectories, but the distance and direction of their flights are limited, both by the size of the ball and by the confines of the area in which the game is played. Golf, by comparison, is far less restrictive. There are many records of balls travelling well over 350 metres – in 1974 a Californian golfer, with some assistance from a following wind, hit a mighty 471 metre drive. In addition, the size and shape of the small head at the end of a long steel club make it possible for the ball to shoot away in almost any direction, sometimes right off the course.

The point of this athletic diversion, and the reason that golf provides such an eye-catching illustration, is that the successful golfer has to exercise a powerful capacity to organise randomness. There are many more directions involved than the relatively narrow path of the fairway. Left to chance, a ball is more likely to end up further away from the hole than nearer to it. This is the nature of all random processes, which tend to become increasingly disorganised as time goes by. What life (or God if you prefer) has done, is to come along like an expert golfer and bring astonishing order to such chaos in our part of the cosmos, taming randomness and narrowing down the number of possible paths in the evolution of matter.

The comparison can be taken further. The origin and creation of life on Earth is highly unlikely, an event even more improbable than a hole-in-one at golf. But in one sense there is a similarity. There are many more places on a golf course than the hole in the middle of a particular green and, in theory, a ball driven at random is equally likely to land on any of them. All are equally improbable. However, the fact is that in golf that little hole in the grass has a very special significance – an attraction that is not possessed by other random dents and hollows on or off the fairway. The hole has what amounts to a magnetic attraction for the ball, gathering it in eventually, usually to the accompaniment of applause from spectators who join the golfer in willing it to get there as soon as possible.

Given the complexities of chemistry, there are many more possible combinations of elements than those which produce the twenty amino acids and four nucleotide bases that are involved in the production of all living things. There are also many more places in the cosmos to get together in such a lively way. However, as far as we know or can tell, life evolved and exists only here on this third planet of an insignificant star – ending up in this little hole on the galactic golf course. The whole thing is wildly improbable, against all the laws of chance and randomness, but it happened anyway. Perhaps because, like a golf ball, life had designs on Earth. It arrived here and prospered, maybe even to the sound of cosmic clapping, because it was intended to do so.

I am not necessarily suggesting that the whole thing was arranged by God, or any other Great Golfer in the sky. What I am proposing is that the origin and evolution of life here was not accidental. That it happened because there was a kind of guidance, a force which took a hand in organising randomness, steering events toward a particular goal. It need not have been a hole-in-one. I suspect that other practice sites, perhaps even in our own solar system, may have been tried en route, but there was no sense of occasion, no real achievement or applause, until it ended up here.

I appreciate that in saying this I am guilty of turning back the scientific clock, returning to a pre-Copernican time when Earth was seen as the centre of the universe. Astronomically, we know that it is nothing special – a tiny planet circling a minor star on the edge of an ordinary galaxy. However, given what has happened here and the odds against it taking place at all, it is difficult to avoid feeling that we and it are something rather special.

We know, from spectral analysis of the space between the stars, that organic molecules exist out there. Recent observation of the nucleus of Halley's Comet has shown that it is surprisingly dark, covered it seems by a layer of sticky tar. Most scientists now accept that such materials are complex enough to be the seeds of life, which may even have been planted here by a passing comet. A few believe that the seeds must by now have germinated elsewhere as well. The problem, however, remains one of recognising life when we see it – which, surprisingly, is not as simple as it sounds.

Life, as we know it, consists of a distinctive set of 'left-handed' molecules and a few special sugars. If you find all these, and nothing but these, in a sample taken from space – then you would be justified in concluding that the substance is (or was) alive. But things are seldom that simple, and nobody has yet found anything like such rich chemical evidence anywhere outside our planet. A more promising characteristic of life, and something well worth looking for elsewhere, is its 'oddness', its tendency not only to break the rules of physics and chemistry, but to do unusual and unexpected things.

Imagine, in the memorable image evoked by Graham Cairns-Smith, a spacecraft brought to a soft landing on another planet. It sits there, taking pictures, sending information home, disturbing the ecology as little as possible. The pictures show nothing but sand and three large and solid-looking rocks. Nothing happens for a while, but then one of the rocks rolls over to the spacecraft, knocks on the side and says, 'Would you like to join us? We're trying to make up a foursome.' You would soon decide that there was life on the planet. You wouldn't need to analyse the chemicals in the rock. Its behaviour would have been sufficiently odd to lead to such a conclusion. Oddness, in itself, is enough to make life recognisable, to set it aside from the ordinary run of things that follow random processes and never dream of scoring below par.

There is something about Earth that lets such dreams come true. Something odd enough in its own way to attract incipient oddness in the cosmos and give it a suitable home.

The French novelist and diplomat Jean Giraudoux once said that 'a golf course is the epitome of all that is purely transitory in the universe; a space not to dwell in, but to get over as quickly as possible.' Looking at natural history, it sometimes seems to me that our corner of the cosmos is a bit like that course; and that there is, as it were, a flag on our little green planet that stands out beyond the galactic hazards and indicates the existence and position of the hole into which the ball of life must eventually fall.

There is a strange and wonderful inevitability about it.

4

秩序と無秩序

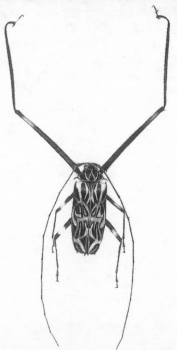

FOUR

ORDER AND DISORDER

Chaos prevails. Or at least it seems to.

Disorder is the rule in our universe, where the final and natural state of things is a completely random distribution of matter. Any kind of order is unnatural and happens only by chance, but that is not the same thing as saying that it happens by accident. There is a vital difference.

When Alexander Fleming left a culture of *Staphylococcus* germs uncovered for several days in 1928, that was an accident. When some spores of *Penicillium* mould happened to settle on the culture during this time, that was chance. However, when Fleming noticed that the fungus seemed to be inhibiting the growth of the bacterium, and decided to subject it to further tests, that was something else. Fleming quite rightly objected to those who described his discovery of penicillin as an accident. 'Chance,' he said, 'favours the prepared mind.'

In 1895, the German physicist Wilhelm Roentgen was examining a cathode-ray tube in a darkened room when he noticed that a sheet of paper some distance away glowed when the tube was turned on. It was by chance that the paper happened to be coated with a luminescent chemical. It was also an accident that led to this paper being in the same room at that time. But neither can account for the fact that Roentgen took the paper into the next room, pulled down the blinds and found that it continued to glow there as long as the cathode ray was in action. He concluded that the tube in the first room was producing invisible radiation that was nevertheless powerful enough to penetrate a wall. Roentgen called the unknown force X-ray and, when asked later what he thought at the time of his 'accidental' discovery, answered somewhat peevishly, 'I didn't think; I experimented.'

A few months later, a French physicist did some experiments of his own. Henri Becquerel wrapped photographic film in heavy black paper and put it in sunlight for a day. It remained blank. But when crystals of a luminescent salt, one that emitted light after exposure to the sun, was placed on top of the package, a foggy silhouette of the chemical appeared on the developed plate. Becquerel concluded that, in the presence of sunlight, luminescent material produced X-rays of its own, and he decided to test other chemicals with similar properties. He prepared several packages of wrapped film covered with uranium salts and left these in a dark drawer while waiting for the sun to shine. By chance, the whole of the last week of February 1896 in Paris was grey and gloomy. By March 1st, Becquerel was becoming restless and decided to develop one of the unexposed plates anyway as a control. To his astonishment, it was strongly fogged as a result of contact only with the uranium. He had 'accidentally' discovered radioactivity.

Fleming, Roentgen and Becquerel all received Nobel prizes, not for accidental discoveries, but for hard work and sound scientific practice that led each of them to take advantage of the chances that came their way. It is clearly unfair to describe such great finds as 'lucky', yet there is reason to believe that good fortune involves something more than just an ability, or a willingness, to take advantage of chances that are offered. There is also some evidence to suggest that we do not all get the same chances. Some people seem to be accident-prone. Which shouldn't really surprise us. Given the relatively short length of individual human lives, it is probably inevitable that some of us will turn out to be favoured, while others tend to slip between peaks in the cycles of fortune.

Science has problems with luck, which it tends to dismiss as superstition, or as a misinterpretation of the idea of chance. It is difficult to find scientific justification for feelings which suggest that some people are dogged by a mysterious influence – a force for good or bad, which follows them like a shadow – and yet such things keep cropping up. Some people do appear to have an edge on their fellows. In the words of a Texan oil millionaire, 'I'd rather be lucky than smart, 'cause a lot of smart people ain't eatin' regular.'

The world is full of such surprises. Each time we look really closely at the chaos of creation, we stumble across totally unexpected patterns in the process. Order where there should, by law, be nothing but increasing entropy. Albert Einstein expressed his surprise very well in the comment that 'The most incomprehensible thing about the world is that it is comprehensible.' To which Bertrand Russell added, 'The final conclusion is that we know very little, and yet it is astonishing that we know so much, and still more astonishing that so little knowledge can give us so much power.'

There is no logical reason why there should be any kind of order or pattern in the universe. And yet there obviously is. Things, from snowflakes to spiral nebulae, take on definite forms and shapes, moving to rhythms which can be defined by surprisingly simple equations. Light has a constant speed and moves in straight lines. Despite the lack of any rational justification, large parts of existence are so neatly ordered that we ought to be going around with permanently raised eyebrows. The fact that we exist at all is proof of some kind of order. A sort of fortunate predisposition that the French historian Jules Michelet highlighted in the observation, 'How beautifully everything is arranged by nature. As soon as a child comes into the world, it finds a mother who is ready to care for it.'

The child, of course, is a product of the mother, just as we are all products of nature. It isn't luck that gives us lungs on a planet that happens to have an atmosphere. The two things are connected, evolving together (if there is any truth in the Gaian hypothesis), in the body of the same super-organism.

Which brings me to perhaps the biggest surprise of all. The new physics of quantum mechanics stresses the randomness of fundamental particles, showing that certain of their properties are determined by pure chance and can never be predicted or measured. Yet it also allows of a certain degree of order which, it suggests, is created by the mind. The universe, in other words, has some precision – but the mathematics are not independent of your mind or mine. It is we who, with our minds, determine the final shape of reality. Which is not to say that the world is 'all in the mind'. It would be more accurate to suggest that the mind is all in the world. That it is part of the world, in fact, because we are intimately involved.

This is beginning to sound rather mystical. What it means in practical terms is that we have a say in how things turn out. We are responsible for part of the orderliness around us and, while the universe as a whole may depend on chance and turn on accidents, we can take the small chances that come our way and shape them to our own ends. And this doesn't depend on accidents.

The fortunate ones, some of those who go on to win Nobel prizes, are merely those who are most responsive to their surroundings, most closely in tune with the cosmos.

You can be lucky if you want to be.

5

存在と意識

FIVE

BEING AND KNOWING

We don't know who discovered water, but we can be sure that it wasn't a fish.

You have to be outside something, able to experience it from a distance, before it makes sense. It is usually the islander who sees the mainland most clearly. If it were not so, then fish would know more about water than fishermen.

Our crowning glory as human beings seems to be our ability to use our brains in a very special way – as instruments of understanding. Not only of the world about us, but of one another. We have the capacity to see ourselves and to put ourselves in someone else's place. We are not only self-aware, but conscious of being so.

Consciousness is the key. It is the power which motivates and drives all human affairs. It is essential, we could not be human without it, but it is very difficult to either describe or to understand. Some of the best keys to understanding come from arguments about where consciousness begins. Who has it and who does not. And in reflecting on this, it pays to do just that – to look at our own reflection in a mirror.

When a human child between one and two years of age is placed in front of a mirror, it shows patterns of behaviour that have been called 'self-directed'. It demonstrates that it recognises the image as one of itself. If it sees the reflection of a hat on its head, it reaches up to touch the original object. Dogs and cats, on the other hand, show no such awareness.

They consistently treat the image as though it were a stranger, something to be sniffed or barked at. They may try to fight it or even to look round the back, as though the mirror were a window, but before long they lose interest and stop reacting at all. This is not necessarily a measure of intelligence. The animal is alert and aware enough to respond to the reflection, but it seems to be incapable of grasping the concept of image-out-there as a reflection of self-in-here. There is no great physical difference between the images produced by dog or man, but there is a huge difference in their perception. Consciousness, in other words, is largely in the eye and the mind of the beholder. And the only consciousness we can be sure of, is our own.

There is, however, one fascinating experiment which suggests that we might not have exclusive rights to it.

At Santa Barbara in California, psychologist David Premack has been involved for many years with studies of a female chimpanzee called Sarah. The main thrust of his work has been to teach the chimp a graphic and synthetic language involving the use of plastic tokens to make up messages on a magnetic board. Sarah does this astonishingly well, demonstrating an impressive awareness of the abstract concepts of 'sameness' and 'difference'. However, her response to complex images is even more interesting.

Sarah enjoys television, so Premack showed her a series of videos involving a human being in some sort of trouble. The tapes featured someone feeling cold; or feeling frustrated by their inability to escape from a locked cage; or feeling angry at their inability to get a gramophone to make music. These were all situations familiar to the chimpanzee, who had felt just such emotions in the past. The test was to see if Sarah could identify with the problems, sympathise with the human dilemma, and offer some solution.

Premack gave Sarah access to possible answers in the form of a warm blanket, the key for the cage in question, and a connecting lead for the gramophone. He found that she could indeed respond appropriately to the pictured dilemmas, choosing the right solution and offering it to the human in trouble.

However, Sarah would only make such a choice, she could only forge the emotional link, if the individual involved was someone she liked!

Premack concluded that chimpanzees do indeed have insights into the way their own minds work, and are able to imagine from the inside what it is like to be in someone else's place. By her actions, Sarah was saying, 'I understand your problem and this is what I would do about it if I were you.' She was showing what looks very much like true consciousness.

It would be wrong and unreasonable of us to insist that only humans can, by definition, be conscious. Anyone who has had the good fortune to work closely with any of the great apes or one of several species of toothed whale, will be in a position to support Premack's conclusion. Some other animals are apparently capable of self-directed behaviour and self-awareness, but none of them have taken this talent as far as we have. No other species ever seems to have been placed in a situation that put such powerful selective pressures on the evolution of the mind.

Oxford philosopher Nicholas Humphrey thinks that most theories of human evolution have got their facts upside down. He asks, 'What are minds for? Why have they evolved in this way rather than another? And why have they evolved at all, instead of remaining quite unchanged?' Humphrey suggests that such development has little to do with tool-making, spear-throwing or fire-lighting. He recognises the importance in our development of an upright stance and a good grasping hand, but concludes that the real hallmark of humankind is our ability to relate to others around us. We are what we are, because we are conscious of and understand each other.

About six million years ago, we made a great leap. As the climate changed and the forests of Africa receded, a rich new ecological niche became available on the grasslands. In theory, any of the ancestral apes could have gone out to take advantage of this opportunity. In practice, there was only one that had the necessary equipment. Only one whose brain was big enough to cope, not only with the physical demands of the savannah, but with the psychological processes involved in maintaining the sort of close-linked society necessary to succeed in the new environment.

This was the parting of the ways. The beginning of communal life centred on a home base. A life involving division of labour and a sharing of food. A society in which relationships were essentially monogamous and long-lasting, in which both sexes helped to rear the children. A community in which skills were dedicated to the group as a whole and passed on by tradition. A culture in which every part of life was socially conditioned. In short, a world impossible to live in for any animals that were not extremely good at understanding one another.

At times it seems as though we fail to understand one another very well. Wars and famines and social disorder suggest that we lack any real fellow-feeling. But, as Humphrey points out, we persistently underestimate ourselves. 'A marriage, a friendship, a workplace partnership, indeed almost every relationship we embark on, testifies to our remarkable human social skills. No animals make friends or work together at the level human beings do. No animal could sustain a human marriage. None would dare.'

We make mistakes, but for all these we also show astonishing insight. Even the least of us, in almost every aspect of our daily lives, is still capable of an intuitive understanding of the human brain that is far superior to anything which a century of intensive scientific psychology has yet managed to provide.

We are gifted with a mysterious inner eye that makes it possible for us to read our own and other people's minds. We 'know' things – even if we don't know how.

ONE MAN'S MEAT

6　人間の糧

SIX

ONE MAN'S MEAT

You are what you eat. More or less.

Anthelme Brillat-Savarin, the politician and gourmet, said, 'Tell me what you eat and I will tell you what you are.' He was thinking mainly of the class distinctions which, in eighteenth-century France, were clearly revealed by a family's choice of food. Workers ate bread and oysters, while the nobility dined on cakes and poultry. Today the reverse is true, but there is still a great deal that can be learned about any creature from its diet.

The average human stomach has a ton of food in it each year, so it is hardly surprising that food should interest us as much as it does. More of our waking hours are spent in feeding than in any other single activity. Our days are divided into convenient portions, each separated from the other by a break for taking some kind of food. Furthermore, often the portions between the breaks are filled with the effects of the last meal or thoughts of the next in a chain of more than a thousand meals that punctuate each year.

Rich or poor, we are obsessed by food. It has always been this way. In fact, it was this preoccupation which was directly responsible for us becoming human at all.

To understand this quirk of evolution, we must go back a little way. Back about 150 million years to a time when dinosaurs were dominant and the land was decorated with cycads and giant tree ferns. The ruling reptiles were the most conspicuous part of Mesozoic ecology, but in the undergrowth things were beginning to buzz. New orders of insects were evolving rapidly from the first wingless forms and, amongst them, the most successful were the Hymenopterans – a group consisting of the wasps, bees and ants. Together, these little creatures with their membranous wings make up just six per cent of the total number of insect species in the world. However, their assembled forces form perhaps twenty per cent of the weight of all land animals, including elephants and men, and they have succeeded in invading and altering most of the habitats on Earth.

The secret of this extraordinary success lies in the fact that wasps, bees and ants are intensely and uniquely social. With the exception of termites, they are the only insects which show higher social behaviour – just as we are the only primates ever to get together in large groups which practice division of labour. Like the wasps, we seem to have been brought to this point by the same stimulus. By our preference for certain kinds of food.

Early wasps were, it seems, essentially neophilic, quick to adapt to the fact that the world about them offered a range of other insects, all of them edible. To begin with, individual wasps attacked and ate prey far smaller than themselves. Modern male wasps still do. But somewhere along the line, probably during the Jurassic, some wasps became more ambitious and invented *haplodiploidy*. Males in these species hatch from unfertilised eggs and are haploid, having only a single set of chromosomes. Their size is small and their appetite and protein needs are limited. The females, however, are diploid, develop from fertilised eggs, have a double set of chromosomes and grow very much larger. Right from the beginning, their size and appetite made it possible for them to take advantage of the larger meals offered by bigger insect prey. This made them more directly successful, but they also benefited in another and less expected way.

Sister wasps are more closely related to each other than they are to their mothers or their daughters, so it was not long before groups of these successful sisters began to get together to exploit this genetic advantage by giving each other a helping hand. At first this must have been a simple association, but what happened eventually was that some of the sisters spent so much time in service that they became sterile and formed a caste dedicated to nothing but the rearing of their siblings. It is this caste structure, which began simply as a way of getting hold of bigger meals, that today provides the essential basis for all social organisations in insects everywhere.

We seem to have benefited in much the same way. In our case, the sexual division of labour produced larger males who specialised in acquiring larger parcels of food. The men hunted while the women gathered. We have begun to realise the importance of the women's role in providing two-thirds or more of any early family's diet. Nevertheless, the fact remains that fresh meat was the richest and most desired source of protein and fat, and conferred, as it still goes, the greatest prestige on its owners and providers. So there was evolutionary pressure in favour of bigger men and larger meat meals, which resulted in the pursuit of bigger and more dangerous prey.

Our ancestors undoubtedly caught mice and lizards a lot of the time, but they soon became unusual amongst competing carnivores in that they were successful also in capturing prey larger than themselves. Nothing was immune. They killed giraffe and elephant and succeeded in doing so partly because of new improved weapons, but largely because they became social and took to hunting in packs.

There is a direct link between social hunting and prey size. Lions also succeed in subduing big-game animals such as buffalo, and it is significant that they are the only social members of the cat family. They and we, and a few dogs and wolves, are alike in that we often slaughter surplus prey, sometimes store solid food, feed part of it to our young, and tend to practise both cannibalism and intergroup aggression. All these things seem to go together and, in our case, such selective pressures have been responsible for shaping our characters through ninety-nine per cent of human evolution.

Cooperation between early human hunters, and later between groups of hunters in pursuit of larger prey, created the need for a more complex signal system, helping give rise to a sophisticated vocal language. This, in turn, allowed greater cohesion during the hunting process and during the sharing out of any successful kill. Furthermore, the larger the size of the prey, the longer the hunters involved must have lingered in the area, practising and refining their new social skills around a communal campfire.

Humans and wasps seem to have been poised on the edge of an evolutionary divide. They were raring to go. Both started with the advantage of having hands or mouth parts which made it possible for them to manipulate their environment in important ways. However, the spur which seems to have sent both humans and wasps shooting off along lines of rapid and social development, was a hunger for high protein. While it is easy, perhaps even necessary now, to become more vegetarian, it is worth remembering that it was a specific need for meat that made us what we are, giving us an advantage over our cousins the apes, who never went through a stage of conspicuous carnivory.

In Shakespeare's *Julius Caesar*, Cassius and Brutus worry about the rise of their fellow Roman and wonder 'Upon what meat doth this our Caesar feed, that he is grown so great?' The answer, then as now, was not one of quality. Not a question of beef or lamb or even woolly mammoth. It was the quantity that mattered.

It was always a matter of more rather than less.

THE TROUBLE WITH SEX

7 セックスの難点

SEVEN

THE TROUBLE WITH SEX

Is sex necessary?

Well, is it? More than half the world manages without it. For most living things, sex is an unknown or very rare event.

Reproduction is perfectly possible without sex. In fact, in many ways it is far more efficient. A mother who makes do without males may have only female offspring exactly like herself. She lacks that extra chromosome which, in most species, is responsible for making males. She will, however, have twice as many daughters as any other mother who wastes half her time and substance making sons who never produce, and seldom help to rear, any offspring at all. Sons are expensive. They halve an organism's capacity to reproduce and many species manage very well without them.

The common dandelion is one of the most successful plants in the world. Two thousand species of *Taraxacum* have spread across the globe, pushing their way up through carefully-tended lawns everywhere from Greenland to New Guinea, totally without benefit of sex. The bright yellow flowers are a sham. No pollen is necessary. Each plant produces thousands of windblown seeds which carry precisely the same genetic message – 'Make More Dandelions; Mother Knows Best!'

Many insects, such as aphids and wasps, do the same thing, as do some fish, amphibians and reptiles. Solitary female Amazon molly, *Poecilia formosa*, breed abundantly in aquaria without outside help in any form. In fact, no one has ever seen a male molly. There are thriving all-female populations of the mole salamanders *Ambystoma platineum* and *Ambystoma tremblayi* in Canada and New England. In the deserts of Arizona and New Mexico, there is a whole family of exclusively female lizards that have given up sex altogether. Such species are so successful that it becomes necessary to ask why anyone should bother with sex at all.

The trouble with sex is that it is antisocial. Ideal societies, those in which there is perfect cooperation and absolutely no conflict, exist only amongst clones – where all the members are identical. Many of the sisterhoods formed by bees, wasps and ants enjoy such harmony. Or at least they do until sex rears its ugly head.

Sexual reproduction involves individuals who are not genetically identical. It takes place between sexes that are different and must experience a conflict of interest. In the race for genetic advantage, males win by spreading their genes as widely as possible, mating with as many females as they can. Females, on the other hand, profit by depriving males of this variety and keeping them close enough to help raise the young. The offspring in their turn gain advantage for their genes by becoming ever more demanding, insisting on the services of their parents for as long as possible, preventing them from raising a second and competing brood. The adults fight against these constraints by enforcing weaning and by chasing their young away.

So it goes on. Sex and courtship in all animals is a delicate balance between attraction and aggression. Bonds form between individuals despite sex and not because of it. Social ties grow only with the greatest difficulty. Most family relationships are unstable and go through periods of intense conflict. Some survive, but do so only with luck and the exercise of rare intelligence. And at the heart of all this trauma lie the inequities produced by sex.

So why bother with it?

There is no easy answer.

The lusty Henry Miller insisted that 'Sex is one of the nine reasons for reincarnation . . . the other eight are unimportant.'

It is easy to sympathise with such a simplistic view. In order to get two separate individuals to put their lives and sanity at risk, nature has made the act of sex attractive enough to overcome some of its frightening consequences. But what was it that made such awesome risks worthwhile in the long term? There have to be other compensations.

The most obvious advantage of sexual reproduction is that it introduces variation. It mixes the genes up a bit. Asexual populations expand more quickly, but sexual ones enjoy the benefits of flexibility. Slight differences in their offspring make it more likely that practitioners of sex will be able to meet new environmental challenges with some appropriate response. The hope is that one of the kids will come up with a bright answer. Sex makes time and evolution go faster. Or at least it does in theory. The trouble with this argument is that it works only for very large populations over a very long period of time. Despite the amount of sex going on, evolution still takes place surprisingly slowly. Our environment and our biology simply don't change quickly enough to make sex pay.

So what does?

William Hamilton at Oxford University has come up with an ingenious suggestion. It is not food or drink or soft music that makes us sexy, but the threat of attack.

Tropical plants, for example, are in constant danger. If they are not being eaten by one of a host of herbivorous animals, they are being rotted away by thousands of plant diseases. It is no coincidence that the vast majority of such plants go in for sexual reproduction – doing everything they can to vary their genetics in search of some form of resistance or protection. In the rain forests of Indonesia, twenty-six per cent of all trees even have distinct sexes, with male and female flowers on separate plants. In temperate Japan, by comparison, the figure is just three per cent.

Large trees and large animals enjoy the stability provided by being big. They find safety in numbers of cells, but their size also slows down their rate of reproduction, and this puts them at a distinct disadvantage against parasites and pathogens that breed and change 100,000 times more rapidly. The

surprise is that there are any elm or elephant left at all. The fact
that there are, suggests Hamilton, is due simply to sex.

By the time that an elephant is ready to reproduce, its
enemies are bound to have evolved the ability to attack it.
Under these circumstances, the worst thing it can do is to
produce an identical copy of itself, which will be just as vulnerable. So what it does, thanks to chromosomal exchange during
sexual reproduction, is to shuffle the genetic pack sufficiently
to produce an offspring different enough to fool the parasites
or cancel out their advantage. Which is why, perhaps, we
humans so often find ourselves drawn to someone who is very
different from ourselves. Opposites attract. Love at first sight
may be nothing more than a powerful and instinctive response
to the smell of another person, whose hormones tell of an
array of distinctive and useful new genes.

Viewed in this way, sex becomes just a defence mechanism.
A way of guarding against attack. What matters is the fact that
two sets of DNA are better at protecting a body than one. All
the rest – the shiny hair, the dewy eyes, the sultry voice, the
shapes and textures of desire – are no more than window-
dressing. Frills designed to bring disparate genes together in
new and vital combinations that protect us from disease.

Sex, it seems, serves the same purpose as drugs. Which
may be why it can become so addictive.

8　知覚の窓

EIGHT

MAKING SENSE

Our planet is being bombarded.

Every second of every day, we are beset by a hundred million impulses which pour down on us as an avalanche of stimuli and information. This barrage ranges from microscopic cosmic waves that come from still mysterious sources, through the short wavelengths of X-radiation that penetrate our bodies, to the wide band of radio frequencies that carry everything from television soap operas to news about distant galaxies in collision.

Most of such information is useless and irrelevant. It means nothing to an organism going about its daily business here, battling for survival against others who are similarly occupied. So we ignore it. We prevent ourselves from being overwhelmed by putting up a series of barriers which filter out all the news we don't need. We take the cosmic confusion and pass it through what novelist Aldous Huxley called 'the reducing filters of our brain and nervous system. What comes out at the other end, he said, is 'a measly trickle of the kind of consciousness which will help us stay alive on the surface of this particular planet'.

In other words, we choose to live. We have to choose, because we could never cope with the universe as it really is. Its booming, boisterous confusion is too much for us, so we carefully select just those bits of environmental information that make immediate sense, that are appreciated by our senses.

What we end up with is a set of sensations that give us a limited view of reality which can nevertheless be surprisingly revealing. However, we should never forget, even for a moment, that it is only a partial view. We live like prisoners trapped in a tower of our own construction, condemned to look out at the world through five very narrow windows. For instance, from all the extravagant fireworks of electromagnetism, our senses select only that very small section of the spectrum that represents visible light – just those few wavelengths which lie between 375 and 775 billionths of a metre. There is nothing special about these wavelengths. It is important to appreciate that nothing sacred in nature occurs between 370 and 380 billionths of a metre. Yet we have no knowledge at all of the first stimulus and perceive the second as an illuminating blaze of violet light.

All sensation is biased in this way, and becomes further distorted by what takes place between the sense organs and the brain. Our awareness of the world is not only highly selective, but also very subjective. We not only tune in to selected bits of reality, but we also shuffle these and sort them out in accordance with our experience and our expectation of them.

When you walk into a room that contains a constant source of noise, perhaps something like a large old-fashioned clock, the mechanism seems very loud. Your brain waves, heartbeat and skin resistance all fluctuate in time with the steady tick-tock. But before long, you stop being so sensitive to it. You tune it out. Your skin resistance remains unaltered and you not only stop being disturbed by the sound, you actually stop hearing it altogether. If an electrode is inserted into your auditory nerve – the one which leads from the ear to the brain – it shows that news of the clock is no longer even being relayed. The clock has been classified as having no news value. It is a constant and uninteresting part of the environment and, acting on instructions, the ear censors it out. It ceases to exist and remains in this sensory limbo until it does something new and interesting like chiming the hour or stopping completely.

We see and hear not only with our eyes and ears, but with

our brains. It is in the brain that we arrange things into categories and patterns, sifting the already limited input and making 'sense' of it. Part of this process involves reaching some kind of understanding about the information coming in by comparing it with our own and other people's previous experience of it. We check with them and reach some kind of consensus – which literally means 'a gathering of the senses'. But it is a melancholy fact that, no matter how widely a description of anything may be validated in this way, it is not necessarily anything like what actually exists out there in the real world. Sensation is an abstraction, not a replication, of reality.

Our perception of a piece of bread, for example, depends very much on how hungry we happen to be. The same coin looms far larger in the minds of poor children than it does in those from wealthy homes. Though it also seems to be true that children as a whole are usually more open to the true nature of things. They see the confusion for what it is, without shaping it in ways that adults find more socially acceptable.

Imagine, for a moment, a child who wakes just before sunrise in the country and goes out to a sylvan glade on the bend of a river. He listens to the dawn chorus, watches the mist rise and swirl over the water, smells the rich dampness of patches of fresh white mushrooms in the dark soil along the banks, tastes the bloom on a wild grape growing on a trailing vine, washes his face in the cool water, stretches like a cat, feels the temper and flow of blood through his muscles and laughs out loud. He comes home late for breakfast and his mother demands to know where he has been. 'Out.' And what has he been doing? 'Nothing.' When forced to give some adequate reply, he might say, 'Picking grapes,' but this is nothing more than the sort of functional answer that adults seem to need. The child knows how inadequate everyday words and normal constructs are for identifying and describing any total sensory experience.

There are levels at which we can shape our limited access to the world in highly creative ways. It is, in the end, we who give the rose its scent and the nightingale its song. 'We are the music,' said the poet T. S. Eliot, 'while the music lasts.' Just as a sculptor takes personal responsibility for releasing just one of the many potential statues that are trapped in a block of stone, so it is up to us to reveal the beauty in nature and in data. And, it seems, the best way to do this is to give free rein to our inherent ability to combine the senses and make symphonies out of stray notes.

Nature on its own is colourless, soundless and scentless. It makes no sense. Until it has been sensed, it is nonsense. But, despite the censorship of the senses and the in-built bureaucracy of the brain, we are all born with a very special talent. This, more than anything else, is what makes us human and gives us precedence. We have an inherent and childlike talent for synaesthesia, for putting things together in new and unexpected ways, creating bypasses round the reducing valves.

We know ways of widening the five narrow windows of the mind and can, if we wish, blow the roof right off the prison building.

9　見ることの真実

NINE

SEEING IS BELIEVING

We don't see with our eyes. It is the brain that sees – and chooses what it wants to see.

A camera, with the help of its shutter and lens, captures a picture, but all the processing is done via the film. So it is with our eyes. Light patterns fall as images on the retina, where they become scrambled into electrical signals which travel along a million nerve fibres from each eye to the primary visual centre of the brain. Here, 100 million cells shuffle and sort the signals, re-routing some to deeper areas, but passing most directly on to the cortex – a little pocket of tissue that is immeasurably more complex than anything else that has ever been discovered in the universe. It is this incredible nerve centre that is responsible for vision, which is not so much a replication of the real world as a calculated and very selective abstraction of it.

That perceptive anthropologist Edmund Carpenter has pointed out that we see with the mind's eye, but seem reluctant to admit it. We talk bravely about 'observations' and 'seeing things for ourselves'. We expect all truth to conform to observed experience, as though there were only one way of looking at reality. 'I'm from Missouri,' said American President Harry Truman, emphasising his commonsense and common origins, 'show me.' We still say that 'seeing is believing' and that 'I wouldn't have believed it, if I hadn't seen it.' But the more we learn about the process of vision, the more obvious it becomes that a great deal of the time it would be more accurate to say that 'I wouldn't have seen it, if I hadn't already believed it to be true.'

When Charles Darwin came with his ship into the island channels around Cape Horn, it took a long time for the local people to respond in any way. It looks, from the account in his diaries, as though the Fuegians did not even notice the *Beagle*. They could not see the ship because it was altogether too vast to be encompassed by their imaginations. It was only much later, when several tribesmen had been brought out and allowed to touch the ship and feel the wooden planking of its decks beneath their bare feet, that evidence from an additional sensory centre made the giant vessel real to them and capable of being both seen and assimilated.

Things are programmed into our mental computers so that they make sense to us in the future, purely on the basis of our experience with these things in the past. We discover depth and perspective by touch, and then marry these sensations to those received by sight. Children born without arms or legs have the greatest difficulty all their troubled lives in seeing things in depth. A pygmy from the dense rainforests of Central Africa, where it is never possible to see very far, is astonished when taken out on to the open plains for the first time, to see apparently tiny antelope in the distance. In the perpetual gloom of the forest floor, where sound becomes more important than sight, a pygmy's experience is arranged by a different kind of sense life. He enjoys a separate kind of reality and comes naturally to different conclusions.

Our view of the world is conditioned anyway to an alarming extent by the simple fact of having learned to read. When we shifted from the spoken to the written word, we gave up the ear for the eye. We transferred our interests from the spiritual to the spatial and changed our language accordingly. All inner states in literate societies are now described as outer perceptions. We refer to something being *before*, which means 'in front of', when what we really mean is 'earlier than'. This confusion, along with many others, is a direct result of the subordination of our many senses to one of them, to sight alone.

Simply because we read a lot, which means using only one

sense – and that one in a highly restricted way – we have destroyed the harmonious orchestration of our senses. Reading is hard work and makes great demands on the body. I discovered while teaching schoolchildren in Africa that people need more sleep when they have learned to read; they also need to wear more clothes, suddenly finding it necessary to conserve body heat and energy. However, the biggest shift brought about by literacy is a basic change in the way we see the world.

Literate man orders his experience like words on a page. He scans life from left to right or up and down, just as he scans print. He replaces mythology with history and dismisses dreams. His artists are expected to paint what they see instead of what they feel. And his music becomes more linear, more narrative, less expressive. He even takes to sitting in long straight lines in concert halls, looking at music instead of listening to or moving with it. Literate man, in short, lives in a *uni*verse rather than a *multi*verse. He is a scientist rather than a mystic.

All this has been beneficial in its way. Such concentration has given us the benefits of technology, but it has also reduced our versatility and deprived us of true vision, which did not depend on sight alone. We have gone so far now along the visible road that it rules and distorts our grasp of reality. I am sure that you, like I, know someone who has to put on their glasses before talking on the telephone. Under the dictatorship of the eye, all of us are now so thoroughly programmed in our single-minded, short-sighted way that it might be totally impossible for us to respond to anything that wasn't built on the same bias.

It may already have happened. Our astronauts, like people from Tierra del Fuego, may have been confronted even in the early days of the space programme with a totally new life-form, something really odd, and have been unable to experience it at all. The linear programme imposed by sight, and sight alone, could well be inappropriate and prove to be inadequate when it comes to solving a new problem posed by a completely different kind of sensory experience.

A recurrent problem is that most information is now translated into a visual code. Inner experiences are expected to conform to outer perceptions and, if they fail to correspond, then we dismiss them as hallucination – something we see as fruitless and misleading, rather than as a valuable exercise which involves a productive wandering of the mind. Anything that cannot be clearly seen, we insist, has not been sensed. It must be nonsense. And that, in itself, is dangerous nonsense. To keep one jump ahead of the game, we need a new approach, new attitudes and even a new vocabulary. At the moment we have none of these things, but they are certainly not beyond our neophilic creativity.

What we need is less sight and a lot more insight.

10 耳寄りな話

TEN

NOW HEAR THIS

Ears were never meant for hearing.

Fish and tortoises manage perfectly well without them. Most early vertebrates possess only a rudimentary version of the fluid-filled canals that now form part of our inner-ear system, but which began simply as organs of equilibrium. Such organs respond to gravity and tell an animal which way is up. Later during evolution, in some more advanced reptiles, these canals became more complex and were set in different planes to detect rotational movements of the head. These were useful for maintaining balance. Then finally, almost as an afterthought, birds and mammals added middle and outer ear structures to the earlier systems and learned to respond to a variety of external sound.

The sequence is clear, but the mechanics of the last stage, the development of hearing itself, remains mysterious.

Put very simply, the ear receives sound vibrations and turns these into nerve impulses which are transmitted to the brain. Audiologists have worked out the details of transmission – following the stimuli from the ear-drum past the little bones of the middle ear, through the fluids and sensory hairs and membranes of the inner ear, and along the complex pathways between the cochlear and the auditory cortex of the brain. Just as sight has been tracked down to the brain and not the eye, so it is with hearing. It is the brain that listens and responds. The trouble is that even the most sophisticated of current theories about hearing fails to explain how the system – which translates all complex vibrations into simple patterns of electricity – can make such delicate distinctions between three basic qualities of sound.

Human ears respond to a range of frequencies between 20 and 20,000 cycles per second, making accurate assessments of about 1,600 different wavelengths. But they also do a lot more than that. They assess the amplitude of a sound, discriminating between 350 different intensities ranging from the quietest to the loudest sounds that can be heard. They also appreciate tonality, sensing the quality, timbre and purity of a sound, listening to the differences which take place when a sound is produced by a voice or a flute or a piano string.

Theories of hearing not only fail to account for the ear's frequency response or to explain how we tell the difference between a fundamental note and its harmonics, but they seem incapable of accounting for our abilities to single out one sound from a battery of conflicting noise and to locate the source of this sound accurately in space without moving our heads. We can accomplish all these things and frequently do, confounding science every time we zero in on a particular voice in a crowded room, identifying the speaker, isolating his words from the surrounding babel and making sense of what he says without giving any outward indication that we happen to be eavesdropping.

What we hear under such circumstances is not what is out there. A microphone or a hearing-aid comes nearer to the truth, recording the full and incomprehensible effect of the confusion. The brain, however, discriminates and selects, refining reality in a totally artificial way, telling us only what it may be suitable and useful to know. It is clearly the brain that hears, rather than the ear, but now comes evidence that the ear itself may be much more than a passive microphone.

At the University of Buenos Aires in Argentina, a young Italian engineer has come up with a fascinating theory. Hugo Zuccarelli suggests that ears are active organs and not only receive sounds, but transmit them as well. Ears, he says, hear by making sounds of their own.

It has been known for some time that healthy human ears emit characteristic noises. These have been recorded at the Universities of Keele in England and Groningen in Holland. They range in frequency from 1,000 to 2,000 cycles a second and sound like high-pitched whistles. Different people produce different frequencies and the same person can emit a different frequency from each ear. Under normal circumstances, no one is conscious of the sounds they make, but you can sometimes get just a hint of your own transmission in a soundproof chamber or on a quiet day in the country. I vividly remember becoming aware of my own private broadcast while sitting on a dune on a windless day in the hot silent wastes of Death Valley in California. It is a sound that must be what the poet John Milton described as a 'dismal universal hiss'.

Zuccarelli's insight suggests that we don't listen at all to the sounds of the natural world, but respond only to the patterns produced by interference between those sounds and our own transmissions. In other words, we send out a reference wave which interacts with incoming signals and sets up a sort of acoustical hologram – and it is this that we listen to and analyse. We do not hear the sound that is outside, we hear its recreated pattern inside.

Zuccarelli points out that the most sound-sensitive creatures have asymmetrical ears. Owls' are distinctly lop-sided. One ear is higher and larger and further forward than the other, creating a discrepancy between the information transmitted and received by the two, which makes it possible to locate the source of a rustle made by a small rodent as it scurries by in the dark. An owl can locate a sound to within one degree while still looking straight at it.

The same lack of symmetry is true of human pinnae. Nobody, not even the most admired fashion model, has identical ears on each side of her perfect head. We are basically asymmetric and have peculiar and otherwise inexplicable folds in our external ears. The shape of these, says Zuccarelli, is concerned primarily with the way in which they transmit sound and only secondarily with the way they receive it. Our squashed-up ears can hardly be regarded as ideal instruments of amplification and it certainly makes more sense to see them instead as structures designed for idiosyncratic sound transmission and pinpoint sound location. Experiments with microphones placed in large artificial ear-shapes seem to turn out better orchestral recordings. Or seem, at least, to produce recordings that make better sense to human listeners, who are then more easily able to place the position of the individual instruments involved.

The possibility of two-way interaction in hearing begins at last to make sense of the ability of some people to 'see' with their ears. Those who are blind from birth develop particularly acute hearing. One woman tested in Derby in England in 1981 proved that she could walk through the woods without bumping into trees or falling over logs, and could distinguish on the street between stationary cars, trucks and vans, sometimes even identifying their make. It was only as she began to grow older and lose her auditory acuity that she complained 'I can no longer hear the silence of lampposts.'

Our familiarity with the world of sound begins very early. Experiments on pregnant women at Rush Medical College in Chicago show that human foetuses are very much aware of sounds outside their mother's bodies. From the age of twenty-four weeks onwards, they produce marked reactions, blinking into the gloom of the womb in direct response to sudden loud sounds. They also seem to be most responsive, turning and grimacing, to the timbre and frequency of the human voice. Suspicion grows that we start to practise auditory skills and even begin to learn our home languages long before birth.

The ear talks, the brain hears and even unborn babies listen.

SOUND EFFECTS

11 音をめぐって

ELEVEN

SOUND EFFECTS

Professor Pierre Gavraud is a successful engineer who works near Marseilles, where he enjoys the respect of his students and colleagues. However, twenty years ago his career almost came to a premature end.

In 1965, Gavraud suffered from severe recurrent nausea. This naturally worried him, though concern turned to curiosity when he realised that the illness occurred only when he was in his office at the top of the institute building. He wondered what it was about the room that disturbed him, and tried to track it down with an array of instruments sensitive to various radiations and toxic fumes. He found nothing. The professor was about to give up and go home for good when he happened to lean against one of the office walls. It was vibrating at a very low frequency.

The source of this energy turned out to be an air-conditioning plant on the roof of a building nearby. Gavraud's room was just the right shape and lay at the right distance from the offending machine to resonate in sympathy with it. He was being made to feel unwell by spending hours in a chamber pulsing with infrasound.

Gavraud was fascinated. He forgot all about feeling sick and turned his whole attention to the phenomenon. He measured the guilty frequency at precisely seven cycles per second and, knowing that human ears are sensitive only to sounds between twenty and 20,000 cycles, wondered why his body should respond in such a way to an extrasensory cue. His first step was to build other machines to produce infrasound to order, and it was one of these that, once again, came close to ending his career.

The device was shaped like an old-fashioned police whistle with a pea in it, except that this one was nearly two metres long and powered by compressed air. The occasion of its first trial is the subject of speculation and shrouded in secrecy, but it seems that the technician who turned it on fell down dead on the spot. It is said that the assistant's internal organs were found, on post-mortem examination, to have been mashed into an amorphous jelly.

Gavraud was shocked, but went ahead nonetheless, though a lot more cautiously. His next test was held out of doors, with all observers screened from the machine in a concrete bunker. They turned the air on very gently, but the results were almost as devastating. The whistle remained inaudible, but it broke every window within a kilometre of the site.

The deadly Frequency Seven Machine was retired or, as some suspect, disappeared into military hands, but interest in the phenomenon continues.

We know now that earthquakes make our whole planet ring like a gong, setting up longwave, low-frequency oscillations that go on for an hour or more and can be measured anywhere on earth. These vibrations occur at frequencies from seven to fourteen cycles per second, and the fascinating thing about them is that they not only accompany, but also precede the actual occurrence of a quake. They provide an early warning system.

People who live on the volcanic 'ring of fire' that encircles the Pacific have long held that earthquakes may be predicted by the aberrant behaviour of rabbits and deer, birds and cats that flee from the zone of an epicentre before the earthquake itself occurs. This folklore is taken particularly seriously in Japan and China, where earthquakes in 1923 and 1977 alone killed 142,000 and 242,000 people respectively. In both countries, bio-sensors are included in earthwatch programmes, with fish – which have the advantage of living in a medium that conducts vibrations even better than air – playing a prominent role.

If there were to be such alarm centres in India, they ought to include an elephant or two.

In 1985, Katy Payne of Cornell University was standing near a group of Asian elephants at the Portland Zoo when she became aware of a strange discomfort, something she later described as 'like the rumble of distant thunder'. Katy had worked for fifteen years with her husband Roger on the sounds made by humpback whales and wondered whether the elephants weren't doing something similar – signalling to each other on a secret channel beyond the range of human hearing.

Between 1987 and 1988, Payne made recordings of elephants both in captivity and in the wild and found, by speeding up playback, that the animals produced distinct infrasonic calls. These sounds are so intense that they easily travel over fifteen kilometres through forest and tall grass, keeping even widely scattered herds in close touch with each other, and making any humans caught in between distinctly uneasy.

As a species, we are relatively insensitive to sounds outside our normal range, but clearly not unaware of them. Gavraud's illness is an extreme example, but from accounts of those caught in earthquakes, it is clear that most people are left with feelings that range from bewilderment to stark terror. Such feelings not only persist long after a quake is over, but tend to reappear before an aftershock or a subsequent quake occurs. In other words, we learn to recognise and respond to unconscious infrasonic stimuli. Those who survive an earthquake become better equipped to deal with the next one.

It seems we are also sensitive to frequencies at the other end of the sonic spectrum.

In 1972, a zoologist out hunting for bats in the British countryside noticed a powerful high-frequency signal on his ultrasonic detector. It was dawn and there were no longer any bats about, but he was able to track the rapid and regular pulse of sound to a nearby megalithic site. He searched the area for signs of life, but found nothing and left with the strange feeling that he had been listening to a conversation amongst the stones themselves.

The Institute of Archaeology at Oxford followed up the zoologist's observation and discovered that, at several sites with prominent standing stones, there were patterns of ultra-sound that were strongest at dawn on any day, but rose to a high-frequency screech that continued for several hours on those mornings in March and October that coincide with the astronomical equinox. Those times when the length of day and night are equal all over the earth have always been considered magical. Times in all cultures for the celebration of planting and harvest, for ceremonies of renewal and thanksgiving, when people gather to celebrate their relationship to the cosmos. Now it seems that we need no priests or calendars to tell us when the time is nigh. The Earth itself gives fair warning.

One of the results of the Oxford investigation has been the discovery that circles of stones, like the famous one at Stonehenge, create an ultrasonic barrier. There is always a background of ultrasound in the countryside produced by the rustle of leaves and grass, but inside the rock circles there is sometimes complete ultrasonic silence. An eerie hush that bursts into the normal clamour as you step back across the ancient boundary once again. It looks as though the stones, or their arrangement, mark or even provide some kind of refuge. A hole in the landscape.

It is clear, from even a casual examination of any of the megalithic sites, that the weighty boulders, the great earth mounds and banks, are never arbitrarily placed nor randomly arranged. These ancient structures follow intricate patterns that seem to relate to seasonal events and may have solar, lunar or stellar significance. Some could even be astronomic observatories or cosmic computers, but none came to be that way by chance. All such sites reflect antique recognition of a place of great importance.

The discovery that sound is made by or behaves strangely at such sites, implies that those who built them were either aware of an existing energetic anomaly, or carried out their work in ways that made it manifest. I am inclined to think we sometimes give our ancestors far too little credit. I suspect they knew very well what they were about and that, before our senses were bombarded with the current electromagnetic confusion, we were more sensitive to the pulse of our planet. Able, perhaps, even to tell when she was not well and to respond to rumbles of infrasound by taking at once to higher, safer ground.

I have a great respect for ancient knowledge. I think that we still have much to learn from our past and suggest that the most successful evolutionary strategies are those which can combine the best of the old with a readiness to accept what is new.

Neophilia can profit, on occasion, from a little unashamed Palaeophilia.

12

この馨（かんば）しきもの

TWELVE

SMELLING GOOD

We have paid through the nose for our intelligence.

Consciousness and creativity are coordinated in the cerebral hemispheres at the front of our big brains. These great bulges occupy the whole of the forebrain, squeezing out those areas which, in earlier mammals, were exclusively concerned with a sense of smell.

It all goes back to time we spent in the trees. In order to be able to jump with safety from branch to branch, we needed a good sense of perspective, and this could only be guaranteed by having binocular vision. So, over millions of years, our eyes slowly migrated round to the front of our heads where their fields of vision overlapped, making it possible to judge distance accurately. However, this new configuration of the face made it flatter, reducing the length of the snout and, with it, our sensitivity to smell. Human noses have just four square centimetres of olfactory tissue compared to eighteen square centimetres in a dog. Along with this reduction in the region of smell there went a corresponding reduction in the importance of that area of the brain, whose functions were usurped by a burgeoning intelligence.

This close association of smell and cerebration may account for the fact that nothing in our lives – no sight or sound, not even the most lyrical theme music – is quite so evocative as an old and familiar smell. The slightest whiff of something as simple as a fresh pastry or a log fire has the capacity to unleash complex memories, bringing whole episodes in our lives vividly to mind. We know this and relish the experience and yet we persist in underestimating our olfactory abilities, perpetuating the myth that we have a poor sense of smell.

Compared to some other mammals, we are indeed microsomatic. Dogs are a million times more sensitive. Experiments have shown that a trained dog can pick up the tracks of its master over grass or sand, rock or pavement, even after hours have passed, just by following the scent of those few molecules of distinctive butyric acid which pass with sweat through the soles of the shoes. The dog can do this even when a dozen other men have walked behind the master, deliberately treading in his footsteps and confusing the trail.

All of which makes one wonder how dogs cope at all with a world rich in confusing and far stronger smells. Why do they not find the abundance of smells unbearable? Why, if their sense of smell is so acute, do most dogs find it necessary to get so close to human beings, even to the extent of giving a stranger a sharp nasal nudge in the groin?

We still have a great deal to learn about the world of odours and chemical signals, which remain largely mysterious, but research in recent years has shed surprising new light on our own abilities.

At Vanderbilt University in Tennessee, pairs of children from the same families were given identical white T-shirts to sleep in for three consecutive nights. On the morning of the fourth day, all the shirts were placed into plastic buckets with small holes in the lids and each child was asked to identify the one out of twenty that belonged to their brother or sister. Eighty per cent of the children succeeded with a single sniff. In a follow-up test with their parents, ninety per cent of the mothers were able not only to pick out the smell of their own children, but could say which of their offspring had worn the shirt in question.

At the University of Philadelphia, test subjects were asked to smell exhaled breath at the end of a glass tube passing through a screen. Eighty-five per cent were able to sex the unseen breather, with fewer mistakes being made when the mystery person was of the opposite sex. We seem not only to have a keen sense of smell when it comes to identifying someone we know, but to exercise a surprisingly fine discernment when dealing with smells that carry some sort of sexual message.

It is known that male saliva carries sex hormones. Such things play a large part in the sex life of pigs, where the boar induces the sow to mate by spraying her with his spittle, but little is known of similar effects on human behaviour. Researchers at Birmingham University in England have tried spraying the male sex hormone adrosterone at various concentrations on to a seat in a dentist's waiting room and found that women patients seemed actively attracted to the pungent chair, while men seemed somewhat repelled, particularly at the higher concentrations.

We seem best able to manufacture and disseminate sexy smells from the hairier parts of our bodies, which are rich in the apocrine sweat glands that produce complex secretions. Our armpits are factories for two powerful steroids, whose taps are turned on at puberty and off at menopause, and seem to be a very useful source of information from our friends, acquaintances and lovers.

In many parts of Europe, traditional folk dances include movements in which the men wave large handkerchiefs about. This looks pleasant and decorative, but what most travelogues fail to record is the fact that, between times, these innocent-looking accessories are worn in the dancer's armpits and are wafted beneath the noses of female partners with highly suggestive intent.

Women are more sensitive than men to musty smells and reach a peak of such sensitivity every month at the time of ovulation. Even women without ovaries can have such sensitivity restored by a simple injection of the female sex hormone oestrogen. So it looks as though we still retain much of our early mammalian ability to regulate or stimulate behaviour via our noses. When female mice are exposed to the hormone-rich urine of a male, the smell triggers her reproductive hormones into action. In American prairie voles *Microtus ochrogaster* this effect is so dramatic that the weight of each female uterus doubles in just two days. If the mice are exposed instead to the smell of female urine, their oestral cycles are disturbed and sometimes inhibited altogether.

There is evidence to show that something very much like this takes place amongst human beings. At the University of Chicago, Martha McClintock has been investigating stories which suggest that women who live together tend to menstruate at the same time. She has identified some women who seem to be hormonally dominant and impose their cycles on others with whom they share a room. In one study, McClintock simply collected sweat from the armpit of such a 'leading lady' and put one drop of this, dissolved in alcohol, on the upper lips of a group of women three times a week for four months. At the beginning of the test period, the group menstruated at random, but by the end eighty per cent of them began their periods on precisely the same day as a woman they had never met.

Female mice clearly gain a genetic advantage by suppressing the reproductive development of their daughters and other females, but it is less clear how synchronisation might help us. Perhaps it is a throwback to a time when we or our ancestors were polygamous and, with all the females in a family ovulating at the same time, there was a better chance of only the dominant woman becoming pregnant.

Whatever the biological reason for this fascinating discovery, it serves to remind us that we are by no means independent of our origins or nearly so insensitive to smell as we might like to imagine. The success of the perfume industry strongly suggests otherwise. It is no accident that the vast majority of perfume products are still based on the sexual secretions of several kinds of cat, a civet and the appropriately-named musk deer.

Sex extends our horizons, but the fact remains that, even without such incentive, we are really quite good with our noses. Sherlock Holmes suggested that a knowledge of at least seventy-five perfumes was essential for a good detective, and there are in fact experts who can identify not only the country of origin of a sample of lavender oil, but even name the farm on which it was produced. We may not be able to describe such differences – even distinctive smells like burning rubber are extraordinarily difficult to put into words – but it seems likely that, with practice, we can distinguish as many as 10,000 different smells and may respond to as few as three or four hundred molecules of any particular substance.

It is enough to make one wonder about the wisdom of covering up so many natural smells with products such as underarm deodorants and polluting our lives by adding potential irritants and unnatural odours to everything from taxis to toilet tissues.

A SENSE OF DIRECTION

13　方向感覚

THIRTEEN

A SENSE OF DIRECTION

Even bacteria know where they are going.

In 1975, a biologist from the University of Massachusetts was studying microscopic life in the marshes of Cape Cod. He noticed that one of the most common microbes there seemed to present itself to him in a constant pattern. No matter how he positioned his microscope or the slide, the rod-like bacteria came to lie parallel to each other, all pointing and moving roughly north.

A few years later, microbiologists in Brazil and New Zealand reported that bacteria and minute unicellular algae in their swamps were similarly coordinated, parading and moving resolutely south. Electron micrographs of such species have now revealed that each contains a magnetite microcrystal, the smallest piece of mineral that can still act as a magnet. All these species have, in effect, tiny compasses and use these to follow lines of magnetic force, navigating down through the murky waters to the rich bottom ooze where they feed.

Mud snails in both hemispheres coordinate their activity to tidal rhythms, but several species have now been shown to orient themselves also in weak magnetic fields, combining a lunar clock with an Earth compass to produce very sophisticated navigational systems – all based on the presence in their bodies of a magnetic material called pyrrhotite. Similar tiny lodestones have since been found in the stomachs of bees and in the skull bones of migratory fish such as tuna and salmon.

Homing pigeons have a deposit of ferritin, a protein capable of storing iron, on the right side of their heads, between the brain and the inner surface of the skull. It has been discovered recently that bones in the nasal area of all human skulls are unusually rich in iron.

Our planet itself is a magnet. A permanent magnet stretching between north and south magnetic poles. No one knows why, but it seems to have something to do with the Earth's core of molten iron and nickel. Anyway, the result is that all of us here live in a magnetic field which fluctuates according to cycles in the sun, but remains stable enough in the short-term to provide a useful source of information. Life is seldom slow to take advantage of such cues.

At Manchester University in England, a long series of experiments with students has shown that most of us have an innate ability to find our way. When taken out like racing pigeons to an unfamiliar place, we still know roughly where we are. Even when blindfolded during the trip, on overcast days, without prevailing winds or any obvious sounds or smells to work with, a surprisingly large proportion of people are able to point in the approximate direction of home. However, this talent is distorted when we are made to wear a helmet that provides a new and different set of magnetic instructions.

We are conditioned, brainwashed if you like, from early life to the patterns which prevail where we were born, and we carry this programme with us for the rest of our lives. Usually it serves us well. When the explorer Captain Cook was finding his way across the Pacific, he had the good fortune to meet a Polynesian priest called Tupaia. This natural navigator was able, no matter where Cook took him, no matter how circuitous the route, even from as much as 10,000 kilometres away, to point unerringly toward his distant home on Raiatea. But that was in the eighteenth century. In those days, our planet's magnetic environment was simple. There was a weak background field like a terrestrial pulse, sculpted occasionally by changes in the sun and moon, and nothing to interfere with this rhythm but a passing lightning storm or two. However, during this century, and particularly during the last forty years, everything has changed.

A technological boom which began after World War II has left us all awash in a sea of strange new energies. Every digital watch, each flashlight and portable radio produces a direct-current magnetic field. The rails of electric trains act like giant antennae, hundreds of kilometres long, broadcasting low-frequency waves over the entire countryside. High-voltage powerlines produce devastating fields that concentrate in metal structures anywhere nearby. The air is filled with the electronic babble of billions of transmitters. And we are all receivers. Everywhere we go, at home or at work, every hour of the day or night, we are bombarded by microwaves from ovens, metal detectors, automatic doors and cordless telephones.

We are, whether we like it or not, involved in a gigantic electromagnetic experiment. The density around us of radio waves alone is already 100 million times the natural level reaching us from the sun. Each day, with every new development in superconductivity and magnetic levitation, we add to an electronic smog from which it has become impossible to hide. As yet, no one knows what the effects of this kind of pollution are likely to be. But we can make quite a good guess.

At the University of Lund in Sweden, zoologists have recently completed an elegant if somewhat unkind experiment that shows what can go wrong. They have been working there for some years on *Ficedula hypoleuca*, the pied flycatcher. This is a plump and engaging little bird that breeds in Sweden, but wisely chooses to spend its winters in the warmth of West Africa. The parent birds set off first on their long migration and the new brood follow some weeks later when their feathers are fully grown. Instinct, and an ability to navigate by sun and star positions, take the young birds safely south across 6,000 kilometres of totally unfamiliar territory to their traditional holiday homes. This is an impressive talent, one which has served the species well for thousands of years, but it is unfortunately and easily disturbed.

The Swedish scientists have found that all it takes to destroy the flycatcher's sense of direction is to expose it, at a critical stage, to an unnatural magnetic influence. They fitted some nest boxes with Helmholtz coils which distorted the geomagnetic field so that, for just the first twelve days of their lives, the chicks lived in a world in which the magnetic pole seemed to lie not in the north, but to their east. This was enough to ruin their lives. When autumn came and it was time for their first migration, the birds became confused. They were living by then under normal magnetic influence, with a clear view of the sky, the sun and the stars, but they ignored the usual cues and chose instead to set off at right angles to their proper migration route. If they had not been restrained, these hapless and brainwashed young flycatchers would have ended up, not in the warmth of West Africa, but frozen to death in the North Atlantic winter.

The chances are that we could become similarly confused.

We are as sensitive to magnetism as any bird. Our control systems are tuned to natural rhythms in precisely the same way as the flycatcher's. We don't necessarily migrate, but we use the gentle cycles of our planet as points of reference in our lives and become very disturbed without them. Experiments in Germany have shown that people kept in mu-metal chambers, which artificially shield them from all contact with Earth's field, become desynchronised and suffer from a variety of nervous disorders. They become stressed, they see things which are not there and fail to respond to others that are.

Maki Takata at Toho University has shown that the level of albumin in our blood serum fluctuates in direct accordance with sunspot activity, which affects us through changes in Earth's magnetic field. We know that industrial and traffic accidents increase, and that more people are admitted to psychiatric hospitals during such natural magnetic storms. However, we are only just beginning to appreciate how far we have gone towards producing similar changes as a result of alterations in our magnetic environment. Mice that spend all their time in mu-metal cages show signs of unusual hair loss, premature ageing and early death. What then of people condemned to spending their lives in steel structures, surrounded by electromagnetic confusion, isolated from contact with the ground?

The evidence suggests that their strength just ebbs away, like that of the giant Antaeus, who defeated all comers until Hercules killed him by simply holding him aloft, cutting him off from the Earth until he became drained of natural energy.

Neophilia on its own is clearly not enough. We need to be very sure of where we stand before we leap. Without a sense of direction, even the best and bravest explorers get lost.

14
超感觉的知觉ESP

FOURTEEN

EXTRASENSORY PERCEPTION

Old Taylor was a farm dog. An important part of the life of a family in East Tennessee. He herded cows and at milking time each day rounded up and brought in the herd and made sure that each animal went into its proper stall. He belonged to the whole family, but was fed and cared for by the youngest son, and became distressed and lonely when the boy went to college 150 kilometres away.

Six weeks later, the dog disappeared from the farm and turned up whining and scratching at the door of the college residence. He had never before left the farm, but managed somehow to find the right door in the only building in 17,600 square kilometres of Tennessee that housed his master. The boy kept the dog for two weeks, but knew that it would be badly missed on the farm. So one day, after feeding Old Taylor well, he took the animal outside and gave the command that always sent him out to round up the cows. Old Taylor went running obediently off, and at milking time the following evening turned up back at the farm and went directly to work, apparently quite content now to do so.

The return journey is easy to understand. The dog was covering ground it already knew, navigating to an established home base. But the task of locating the boy in the first place is beyond ordinary biological comprehension. There were no sensory cues, no geographical or historical features that could have helped Old Taylor find his friend. There is no gene or instinct that can explain such behaviour.

It is not, however, unique.

Chat Beau was a white half-Persian cat. The special pet of an eight-year-old boy called Butchie who lived in Lafayette, Louisiana. The whole family went off one day looking for a new home in the neighbouring state of Texas, and when they returned a few days later, the cat was missing. He had never strayed before, but after three weeks they gave up waiting, left the old house and moved to a new one 450 kilometres away in Texarkana. Butchie started at his new school and four months later a white cat turned up in the yard. It ran away from the other children, but when Butchie appeared, it jumped into his arms. The cat had an old black tar stain on its tail, a familiar scar over one eye and it spent that night sleeping in its usual place between the paws of the family collie dog. It was Chat Beau, who had succeeded in tracking down the boy at his new school on the edge of over 300,000 square kilometres of totally unfamiliar territory.

Such things are pepleximg. Not every stray pet gets re-united with its owners, but it happens often enough to strain the usual explanations of chance or coincidence or mistaken identity. In each case, the only thing the new and old homes have in common is the person or the people concerned. And the fact that they are concerned, seems to be important. There is nothing to link the pet to the house or school arbitrarily chosen in a new town, with which neither pet nor owner have any previous experience. Nothing but an emotional bond between them. In the lack of any more physical explanation, it becomes difficult to deny the possibility that sympathy could be involved.

There is evidence to suggest that individuals who hardly know each other, can nevertheless share an experience. In 1972, physicists at the Stanford Research Institute in California proved this. They built a special isolation chamber deep in the heart of their laboratory and gave it double steel walls thick enough to shield anyone inside from the reception of any light, sound or electrical signal. Into it they placed a man, cutting him off from the rest of the laboratory as effectively as if he had been exiled to Texarkana. Meanwhile, in another room, they set up a second man in front of a machine called a photostimulator – an instrument designed to produce patterns of bright light that flash directly into the eyes of a subject and make his brain-waves flicker along in the same complex rhythm. The subject watching the lights was asked to try to send information to the person in the isolation chamber, who knew only that he was on the receiving end of some kind of signal. Both were attached to the electrodes of electroencephalograms. The results were startling.

Soon after the sender established his photorhythm, which could be seen and checked on the EEG tape, there was an equivalent shift, a sympathetic response, in the brain-waves of the receiver. Although he could not see the sender, the receiver's brain-waves changed from their normal resting state to precisely match those of the man outside, who was being driven by the lights. The person in the isolation chamber remained unaware of any change, but his brain produced patterns beyond control or cheating which record, beyond any reasonable doubt, the existence of some sort of direct connection. The physicists concluded that 'a person can perceive a remote state of affairs', or at least he can if there is another organism involved.

The Stanford experiment remains the only really convincing laboratory demonstration of such an ability, but it is one that crops up fairly regularly in spontaneous situations, most often between people who are emotionally involved – between lovers or between parents and their children.

Examples are legion.

'We were at a football game in Berkeley,' says a Californian housewife. 'My husband got up suddenly in the middle of the game and said we must go home at once as our son had been hurt. When we arrived home, our son had shot himself and we had to take him to a doctor to have the bullet removed.'

A very old lady, suffering from advanced senile dementia, and normally quiet and contented in the ward of a psychiatric hospital, suddenly became restless and highly agitated on the exact day her son, unknown to anyone in the hospital, was charged with murder. A psychiatrist was asked to assess the man's fitness to plead and weeks later he happened to be passing through the hospital on ward rounds, when the old lady, quiet again since her outburst, leapt to her feet and greeted him with unusual warmth and hilarity. It was later learned that the charges against her son had been dropped and he was being released from a distant court at the very moment the doctor passed through the ward.

Individually, none of these reports is more than an interesting anecdote, but taken together, as a body of information which crosses cultural lines and even bridges the gap between species, it becomes more significant. It tells us something about the condition of individuals who happen to be widely separated in space and yet appear to be able to maintain some kind of connection.

There are now enough such accounts on record to be very persuasive. I am convinced that living things, particularly those who know each other well, share a sort of resonance, something that manifests most dramatically in crisis situations. The fact that the link exists and can be used by other species suggests that it is an old one with a long evolutionary history. It wouldn't surprise me if we, who love the new and the newsworthy, should not be able, sooner or later, to find a way of making such connections work on demand and at will.

Don't telephone, just telepath.

CATCHING FIRE

15　火に憑かれて

FIFTEEN

CATCHING FIRE

There are three great leaps in the history of human achievement.

One was the development of language. Another, the cultivation of crops that led to settled agriculture. And the third, perhaps the earliest and certainly the most emotive, was the mastery of fire.

Almost every culture has a myth that recounts the capture and domestication of fire. In each case, flame was sought partly because it was useful, providing warmth and protection against predators; but also because it was fascinating. It still is.

Despite all our sophistication, the minds of our children glow with the simple magic of matches, and even tired adult imaginations are ignited for hours on end by the flickering expressions in a log fire. We are inflamed, just as Peking Man and some of the African ape-men must have been when they first captured the spirit of the sun and danced around it, or simply sat and watched this new and fascinating fetish come to life on the floors of their caves.

Tending fire was a great adventure. Taking it from the wild, from a bush in flame or a lightning strike, feeding it and keeping it alive and well in captivity was a very neophilic thing to do. A brave and impudent act. An act of independence. Probably the first time any species on Earth took evolution into its own hands and made a major change in its way of life. Not because of the pressures of survival or the dictates of natural selection, but simply for the hell of it. Just because it seemed like a good idea at the time.

The fascination persists. We have got down to the serious business of building fires that blaze more fiercely than those in the sun itself, and we have burned our way free from the shackles of gravity. But even now, with all our know-how, a single candle flame can still hold us in thrall. There is something sacred about it. There always was. Fire was Earth's first divinity, enshrined in those early caves on the altar of its hearth. A sacred flame. Something very soon associated with the spirit of life itself. A symbol both of purification and renewal.

Accounts of the origin of fire range from the Apache belief that the first fire was sparked by buffalo hooves thundering across the plains, to the Maori conviction that flame was a gift from a god's blind grandmother, who drew it from her fingernails. In addition, all people, sooner or later, worried about the flame going out and saw the same significance in perpetual fire.

Eternal flames flowered on altars and shrines. In the Temple of Vesta in Rome, worship was possible only in the presence of the goddess of the hearth. As long as the flame there burned, there was a connection between heaven and earth. An open line. If it went out, contact was broken. The Osage Indians maintained a sacred fire in their chief's hut, bringing life and health to all the tribe. The Tonga in South Africa did the same, forbidding anyone but a priest-diviner to tend it. When the chief died, so did the fire, and it was not rekindled until the appointment of a new leader. Throughout Africa, the domestic fire is still extinguished every time a child is born, and lit anew to mark the beginning of a fresh life.

The connection between fire and life, between flame and divinity, is widespread. There are few religions that do not decorate their places of worship with a sacred flame of some kind, and many in which the faithful demonstrate their fervour by seeking unity with the fire, taking a flame into their mouths or swallowing a burning ember. In Fiji and Tahiti, India and Indonesia, Bulgaria and Greece, in Spain and Mexico, people tread barefoot through red-hot coals. Firewalking is nothing new. It was part of the temple ritual in ancient Greece. Pliny the Elder tells of how certain Romans earned exemption from city taxes by walking over live coals. A monk in medieval Florence chose it as his route to canonisation as Saint Peter Igneus. It is well documented in all ages, but nonetheless remains mysterious.

In 1974, a German physicist from the Max Planck Institute in Munich went to Fiji to film fire-walkers in action. On the island of Viti Levu, Friedbert Karger coated the feet of several participants with temperature-sensitive paints that change colour when heated above a certain point. His pictures of subjects walking through the fiery pit, and of one with the courage to stand in it for seven seconds, show their bare feet glowing with the tint that indicates a temperature of at least 600 degrees Centigrade.

Karger later took a sliver of skin cut from a Fijian foot and placed it on one of the hot rocks where it sizzled into instant carbon. Meat usually cooks at about 100 degrees Centigrade. He decided that the ability of living feet to pass the same way without injury must be due to some sort of insulation. The American physicist Jearl Walker ascribes it to the Leidenfrost Effect, which keeps drops of water from boiling away on a very hot stove by letting them dance and skitter for a while on a protective layer of cooler vapour. It is possible that tropical feet are protected in the same way. Fiji and Tahiti are humid enough to produce a layer of sweat between every footfall. On the one occasion when I joined in a Singapore firewalk, I was taken through preparation that involved drinking a great deal of holy water. However, such purely mechanical conjecture begins to seem a little thin in the light of developments during the last few years.

Since 1980, thousands of ordinary people in the United States and Europe, in Australia and South Africa, have been led barefoot and unharmed through four metre beds of red-hot coals in every possible climate and environment. The firewalking ritual, once confined to those who undertook the trial, talisman in hand, as an act of religious faith, has become the latest fad from California. Something done, after an hour or two of instruction, to 'utilise personal resources' and 'intensify latent power'. Firewalking has become yet another manifestation of the human potential industry which is making some people very rich indeed. And yet it works. Once someone believes that walking through fire is possible, it becomes so. It doesn't seem to matter whether the belief is based on religious conviction, on an understanding of Leidenfrost physics, or on getting value for the 15,000 yen invested in one of the new seminars. No one who puts their heart and their mind into the experience gets burned, and all speak later of feelings of elation. Of living, even for the moment, with or like a god.

We know from studies made under hypnosis that blisters can be inhibited by suggestion or, on the other hand, produced in the absence of any stimulus at all. Subjects told that a red-hot iron is in fact a block of ice are able to restrict normal circulation and to suppress the formation of substances that usually produce inflammation. Such a suppression of normal response is sustained at least long enough to cope with exposure to fire, even that of a blowtorch, for ten or fifteen seconds.

The Persian prophet Zoroaster believed that, in the final war between good and evil, fire would cast the deciding vote. Every man, he said, will have to pass through boiling lava and only the just and the righteous will survive. If he could witness the latest craze, he might have to modify that to allow the survival also of all those who have the courage of their convictions, no matter what these might be.

It seems clear that we neophils have unexpected talents. We are able to transcend in ways which are not confined to those few who have the patience and the discipline necessary to learn esoteric techniques. We all have the ability to exercise astonishing feats of self-control. Somehow it seems fitting that these powers should first be brought to common light in the presence of fire, in attendance on the altar of one of our oldest and strongest concerns.

We never could resist a good fire – or a new challenge.

16

エクスタシーへの道

SIXTEEN

TAKING CONTROL

The mantis prays with good reason. He prays his wife won't eat him. She does so often enough to place severe restrictions on mating behaviour. Instinct drives the male mantis to approach the larger female, but his nervous system is just elaborate enough to provide him with a rudimentary brain, a nerve centre capable of recognising warning signals and exercising restraint. The result is that mating in some mantid species is inhibited by the male's fear of ending up as a wedding breakfast.

The female mantis, however, has an easy answer. She gets round the behavioural block, avoiding the growing conflict between instinct and reason, effectively disinhibiting the male and allowing him to copulate without the interference of fear. She first bites off his head.

We have a similar problem. Not just with mating, but with almost everything in our lives. We are at war with ourselves.

It is an evolutionary difficulty. Something that began at about the mantis level. The first nerves, those in worms and early invertebrates, were simple telegraphs, lines of communication designed to coordinate the behaviour of collections of relatively independent cells. Later, in molluscs and insects, these connections grew into more elaborate networks, expanding to form control centres with the capacity to observe and learn. Eventually, with the development of the vertebrates, bodies grew so

intricate and their relationships so complex, that it became
necessary to have separate kinds of nerve systems for dealing
with different situations. Responsibility was split between
internal and external affairs, between things going on inside
and outside the body, and awareness came to be similarly
subdivided.

Our ordinary consciousness is now obsessed with our external environment, with what goes on in the world around us,
and we have become almost totally unaware of what goes on
inside. It has to be so. We couldn't cope if we had to think
about enlarging and contracting the pupils in our eyes, secreting
saliva, producing sweat as the temperature rises, making our
hearts beat seventy times a minute, changing the pace as the
body demands, and measuring out the hormones from our
glands. There would be no time for anything else if we had to
mastermind the process of digestion, squeeze the spleen,
direct the operation of the kidneys and think about the need
for every breath. So, all these functions have been set aside,
taken out of direct awareness and put on automatic. They
have been placed under the unconscious control of a separate
nervous system – the one we call autonomic.

The rest is in the hands of our magnificent cerebral hemispheres. All skeletal muscles, the ones concerned with direct
action and with manipulation of the world about us, are connected to the central nervous system. They do what we want
them to do. Most of the time. This division of labour between
voluntary and involuntary systems is real and very necessary.
Our busy lives would be impossible without it. Nevertheless,
it also creates problems, leaving us with mantis-type dilemmas.
The split between the two nerve systems is now so strongly
entrenched in practice and so deeply enshrined in science, that
the two systems are in great danger of becoming not only
functionally, but biologically distinct.

We have, with our labels on them and our thinking about
them, effectively put the autonomic system beyond self-control
and made it almost impossible to bridge the gap. As a result,
we have come to believe that anyone who claims to be able to
exercise such control must be either a crook or a crank. Science

says that it is impossible to cut yourself without bleeding, or to stop your heart, or to be buried alive and survive, or to walk through fire without being burned. Scientists ignore the news about this type of accomplishment, which is a pity, because such talents are an important part of our neophilic armoury. A part we may never learn to use unless someone comes along and, metaphorically at least, bites off our heads.

Those who break the scientific rules tend to be people with a different mental set. They come from traditions which encourage self-regulation and have few problems with the reconciliation of internal and external needs. Adepts of the various forms of yoga have long practised techniques which make them mindful of the workings of their bodies and put them in conscious control of normally unconscious processes. Their patience and their willingness to submit with good humour to the machines of a few curious scientists has begun to break down our inhibitions and to inhibit disbelief.

The process began in Kansas in 1968 with a certain Swami Rama who succeeded in the laboratory, while attached to all the apparatus we now find necessary to validate our senses, in changing the blood supply going to two patches of skin on his palm and giving these a temperature difference of six degrees Centigrade. Although the areas were just five centimetres apart, one glowed red while the other turned an ashen grey. Then, for good measure, Swami Rama blocked the flow of blood to his heart, stopping it beating altogether for over twenty seconds.

Further studies followed, with the result that students at Oxford have now learned to vary the temperature in their earlobes, up or down, one at a time or both together. Others in Colorado deal with migraine headaches by drawing blood away from their head to their hands. At Baltimore, Detroit and Harvard, subjects practise control over blood pressure without the use of drugs. In Australia, they have brought salivation under conscious control. At Queens University in Canada, one subject has even learned how to fire single nerve cells, just one at a time, from his brain's array of around 10,000 million.

All this body magic is made possible by a simple technique. Abilities that our science still regards as paranormal are being made available to normal control by anyone, just by letting the conscious mind know what is going on at unconscious levels. The technique is called biofeedback.

Biofeedback is a way of learning, or rather of revealing, what the body already knows. It is accomplished by hooking internal processes up to some sort of external display so that you can see what your organs are doing. That is all, but it is usually enough to bring the processes under conscious control. The instruments involved are electrocardiograms, which monitor heartbeat; electromyographs, which measure muscle tension; thermistors, for taking local temperatures; resistance metres, for indicating general arousal; and, most important of all, electroencephalographs for monitoring activity in the brain.

The combined application of these machines has revealed that, in addition to the three recognised states of awareness – those of waking, sleeping and dreaming – there is a fourth state. Yoga adepts, and even those who master such simple techniques as transcendental meditation, show a decrease in oxygen consumption and carbon dioxide elimination, and a reduction in blood pressure, blood cortisone level and muscle tone. At the same time, such techniques produce an increase in skin resistance, in the perfusion of internal organs and in the levels of alpha and theta waves in the brain.

It seems that someone in this alert-but-relaxed condition is experiencing an altered state of consciousness, and there is every reason to believe that this state makes it possible for us to lift some of the censors in our minds and experience the world around us with unusual clarity.

This union of our rival nervous systems opens all kinds of new doors on experience. It removes barriers to true awareness and gives us all access to the kind of understanding that Zen Buddhists know as *satori* or *kensho*, that yogis describe as *samadhi* or *moksha*, and Sufis speak of as *fana*. It is, in short and in fact, a glimpse of the human advantage. A revelation of what it means to be more than a headless mantis. We rise above mere sexual success to take personal control of our own destinies and realise, even if only for a moment, where neophilia can lead.

To ecstasy.

17
生命の季節

SEVENTEEN

IN SEASON

What do plankton yields, stock prices, cheese consumption, building activity, pork sales, snowy owl migrations, UFO sightings, industrial output, non-agricultural employment and the abundance of salmon, field mice and Arctic foxes all have in common?

They each reach a peak exactly every 4.00 years.

The cycle is clear. The reason less so. It seems to have something to do with the fact that spots on the sun also tend to flare up at such an interval.

The Foundation for the Study of Cycles lists 543 rhythms of things, ranging from freight-car orders to teenage suicides, which recur at predictable intervals. These cycles vary in length from 0.251 of a year to 103.00 years, but there are impressive clumps of events at intervals of 3.33, 4.00, 9.00, 9.20 and 11.00 years.

Life scientists are well aware that invisible rhythms govern much that we tend to consider constant in ourselves and in the world around us. All life is in flux and the changes that take place are by no means random or disorderly. We may not be consciously aware of the fact, but each one of us is surrounded by patterns that make the cosmos look like an immensely complex clock with a million hands.

Some of the rhythms are obvious. The tides ebb and flow. Night follows day. The seasons change. However, we are also subject to less overt influences. Gravity rises and falls, air pressure fluctuates, the strength of Earth's magnetic field waxes and wanes. And all these ups and downs find echoes in us.

Our body temperature, blood pressure, respiration and pulse rate, blood sugar and haemoglobin levels, all change constantly, following the sun, reaching a peak every twenty-four hours. The result is that hormone and urine production rises and falls in the same solar rhythm and we become less susceptible to drugs, more likely to fall ill, go into labour, suffer coronary attacks and die in the early hours of the morning.

We also follow a lunar rhythm, rising every 24.8 hours to peak on the twentieth day. This monthly or menstrual cycle is most apparent in women, who even in cities can be restored to natural regularity by sleeping with their bedroom lights on bright, simulating a full moon, for four nights in every 27.3. However, men show similar periodicity, undergoing a regular monthly weight change of as much as a kilogram. In addition, all of us are moonstruck, getting involved far more often in fights, accidents, arson, kleptomania, murder and other forms of lunacy when the moon is full.

Seasonal rhythms are most evident in animals which migrate or hibernate, but even humans show an annual rhythm in body weight change and, in the northern hemisphere, a tendency to be born more often in May and June than in November and December. It seems that we still have a breeding season, and it is fascinating to discover that, even in an area as racially and culturally homogenous as New England, people born in March live longer than those born in any other month of the year – an average of exactly 4.00 years longer, rising to the rhythms of the cosmos like leaping salmon.

It is hard to measure cycles that last longer than a year, but one of the areas in which such studies have been made is that of people's occupations. Most of us have only one major job or profession in a lifetime and, at Manchester University, Professor Alan Smithers has been looking at these for seasonal correlations.

Smithers turned to the British Population Census of 1971 and extracted the data for one in every ten people born and still working in the United Kingdom. Of 1,461,874 men and 842,799 women in employment, a clear majority were born in the spring, with a peak in April and May and a trough in October and November. When individual occupations were examined, Smithers found that architects tended to be born in the spring, secretaries in the summer, miners in the autumn and electricians in the winter.

When the occupations are arranged in social classes, the trends are even more marked. Those in top jobs – professions such as doctors and engineers, company directors and politicians – were born far more often in the spring, which seems to be a time of high aspirations. The birth-dates of teachers, managers, technicians, farmers and nurses cluster in early summer. Most clerks and cashiers have late summer births. There is a strong tendency for unskilled and manual labourers – construction workers, tool operators, cleaners, labourers and maids – to be born in autumn and early winter.

There do indeed seem to be direct connections between occupation, as an indication of personality and destiny, and date of birth. Which is an interesting scientific validation of one of the basic precepts of astrology. The astrological model of the universe is one which treats it as a unity, as a purposeful whole with an inherent order that unfolds in time and becomes manifest in matter. In other words, the pattern of the stars is inevitably reflected in you and I. But astrology doesn't stop there. It is a sort of algebra of life, a formal system of logic which goes on to claim that it can predict what such effects might be.

Smithers asked members of the British Astrological Association to indicate which professions they thought ought to be associated with births at times of the year represented by each of the traditional 'sun signs' that begin their procession on 21 March – which is also the spring equinox and the start of the seasonal year. Without knowing the results of his survey of 2.3 million people, the astrologers correctly predicted the connections shown by authors, clerks, mechanics, cashiers and miners.

One astrologer went further than a seasonal prediction and

suggested that people in the caring professions, such as nursing, would be born under the signs of Taurus, Cancer, Virgo,
Scorpio, Capricorn and Pisces – signs which astrologers desig-
nate as 'feminine and supportive'. On the other hand, trade
union officials would be found under the signs that alternate with
these and are described instead as 'assertive and masculine'.
Incredibly, he was right. The graphs for 35,781 nurses and
trade union officials are as regular as the teeth in a comb and
alternate perfectly with each other with little or no overlap.

In France, the mathematician Michel Gauquelin has found a
correlation between individual personality and the position at
birth of the Moon and the planets Mars, Jupiter and Saturn.
Gauquelin showed that, all other things being equal, those of
us born when Mars is close to the horizon, do tend to be more
martial; while Jupiter in that position tends to make us more
jovial; Saturn more saturnine; and the Moon more romantic.
The English psychologist Hans Eysenck concludes that the
case for this correlation is 'already stronger than that for almost
any area of research in psychology'.

The fact that these are still minority opinions in science,
reflects the difficulty we have with concepts of time that are
cyclical rather than linear. We who live in technological societies
act with urgency, as though time were short, perceive its
transcience as a threat to our economies and egos, and practise
disiplines such as medicine in ways that fail to connect life with
natural rhythms or to equate health with harmony.

It may not be true that emanations from the planet Mars
make a man 'decisive, freedom-loving and a pioneer'. This is
almost certainly simplistic nonsense. Nevertheless, it is beyond
argument that our lives are affected by the whole environment,
including Mars, and it is possible that the position of the planet
at that moment could be indicative of a set of cosmic conditions
which might well predispose an individual to develop along
certain lines rather than others.

We need to revive the concept of time as a process, to see
it as part of the nature of change, and to appreciate how we fit
in. The successful neophil is not necessarily the one born in
the spring, but he or she is certainly the one with the vision

to appreciate, rather than cling to, the passing moment – and to see it in perspective.

We are creatures of a cosmos dominated by heavenly bodies that are, in one philosopher's words, 'Nature's first born thoughts'.

FACE TO FACE

18
顔がものを言う

EIGHTEEN

FACE TO FACE

Stick out your tongue at a baby.

Go on, try it. The result is surprising. Provided that the child is not sick or otherwise distracted, the chances are that the baby will retaliate and stick out its tongue right back at you. Even newborn babies do this, and the response is not just evidence of the irreverence of modern youth. Babies have always had such an ability and are not nearly as helpless or undiscerning as we once believed them to be.

At the University of Miami, psychologists have been testing infant discrimination. They take babies born to black, Amerindian, Anglo and Hispanic parents and, at an age of just thirty-six hours, put them in a stranger's arms. All the babies demonstrate acute awareness, and a complete lack of concern about race or colour. They know another human being when they see one, and focus immediately on the features of the face, watching mouth and eyes intently. All are able to recognise astonishingly fine distinctions of facial expression. The experimenters in Miami have, for the sake of their own analysis and not because of any limitations in the infants, restricted themselves to just three expressions. Happy, with a smile and relaxed eyes; sad, with a pout and a frown; and surprised, with the mouth and eyes wide open.

The experimenters find that the babies are distinctly and characteristically neophilic. They get bored very easily with just one expression and soon allow their attention to wander.

But they look back at the adult face with renewed interest as soon as a new expression is on offer. As soon, for instance, as happy is replaced by sad or surprised. The babies learn to discriminate between these three basic expressions in a matter of minutes and react to each, as they will to a protruding tongue, by imitation. No practice is necessary. Each of the babies tested was able to copy the three test faces so faithfully that an observer could guess the expression on the experimenter's face just by looking at, or even by looking at a photograph of, the baby.

All of us are able to do this from birth. We are ready, it seems, to respond to faces. We know instinctively which parts of our bodies correspond to the parts we see on another, and we are predisposed to mimic what they do. The implications of this are profound. The observation and reaction involved are things of consequence. They rank as high in the baby's world as the deduction made in ours, from watching a ship disappear by stages over the horizon, that the Earth must be round. It is clear that there has to be a good reason for babies to be programmed in this way.

There is. Our brains work harder and learn faster in the first few weeks after birth than they do at any other time in our lives. We come into the world naked, to be sure, but not with blank minds. Our brains come prepared with lengthy questionnaires that have to be filled in, item by item. We are delivered in pre-assembled form, ready to be plugged in to our local cultures. We are capable of living a thousand kinds of life, but need, if we are to survive, to learn the rules of just one in a hurry.

So we are inherently neophilic. Designed to respond with interest and curiosity to that which is new. We are given various inborn skills, but left to sort out the details for ourselves. We are on our own, but we have an edge. We come equipped with the human advantage. We have big brains and a biological bias in favour of attending to what other humans do. We are ready to learn and what interests us most, right from the start, is social interaction. And we take this at face value.

This has a lot to do with our primate heritage.

When two deer meet on a mountain slope or two dogs circle each other at a street corner, their bodies are usually parallel, their heads facing in opposite directions. In such species, the eyes are at the side of the head, widely separated by a muzzle, giving them good all-round vision and bringing their noses close to each other's expressive scent glands. They can also see signals made by the limbs, the trunk or the tail of a rival. However, when our ancestors took to the trees, things had to change. Smell became less important than binocular vision and, as the nose withered, the eyes moved round to the front of the face, making it possible to judge distance more accurately and to jump from branch to branch without falling to the ground.

The result of this shift in emphasis between the senses is that when two monkeys meet, they do so face to face. Most of their signals, together with nearly all of their distinctive markings, are confined to the facial area. They, and now we, face up to, save face, lose face, try to keep a straight face, fly in the face of, or put a brave face on, things. We communicate to an enormous extent by facial expression, and did so millions of years before we learned to speak.

Just watch the way in which people behave when talking on the telephone. They smile, they frown, they raise their eyebrows, their pupils contract and dilate, they blush – and all to no avail. The gestures are totally wasted on the person at the other end of the line, who cannot see them at all. Nevertheless, we can't help giving such ancient signals. They still form a vital part of our communication and we are, to a large extent, lost without them. Which is why it is so difficult to convey any really complex emotion over the telephone. Or, alternatively, why it is so easy to lie to someone who cannot see you.

An ability to communicate with the face is innate. It doesn't have to be learned. A few contrived expressions, like the wink, are picked up by imitation, but all the basic ones are there from birth. Blind children still give excellent smiles, and people everywhere have similar expressions for all the most common emotions. A Bushman, a Bedouin and a Belgian all compress their lips in a tight smile when refusing to reply to an embarrassing question; or grin broadly, so that the pouches of skin beneath their eyes swell, when they are genuinely amused. Such things are part of the only truly international language.

We all use this language and, on occasion, abuse it – deliberately concealing our feelings by faking an expression. Only man does this. All the faces of an ape are truthful, but humans have learned to act and connive. We pretend to be pleased to see people when we are not. We use tears as weapons to manipulate others. And sometimes we succeed. However, in most cases the performance is flawed, even if only minutely, and fails to fool an experienced observer. We give ourselves away by muscle tension, a slightly frozen quality about the upper lip, in a false smile. Or with eyebrows that slope inwards at an angle more characteristic of anger than the outward slope of genuine grief. Such subtle distinctions are now being formally described by ethologists and psychologists interested in communicating more effectively with other species, or with the mentally ill. Fleeting expressions can reveal distress in an animal, repressions in a patient, or give us access to the workings of the hurt mind in an autistic child.

Conscious interpretation of this kind takes time and training, but it is the sort of thing we do unconsciously all the time as we struggle with the niceties of being social. It isn't easy, but that's the price we pay for being human. Bees have no such problems. Each is born with everything a bee needs to know, and fits right into life in the hive like a perfect prefabricated cog. We, on the other hand, start out with a few good moves and a lot of potential. Our great strength is our adaptability. Only the bare minimum is encoded and fixed in our genes. All the rest is open to practice and improvement.

Which is why newborn babies are so astonishingly alert and feel free to stick out their tongues at convention and history.

19

言葉の通ってきた道

NINETEEN

TALKING BACK

Most animals communicate, but only humans speak.

Our world resounds with the babel of roughly 5,000 languages. There are 845 in India alone. Linguists trace all these tongues back to a handful of ancestral forms, but nobody knows where or when speech began. There is information in the fossil record about the origins of tooth patterns, tool-making and bipedalism, but nothing to tell us, not even to the nearest million years, when all the talking started.

In individual terms, it happens very suddenly.

At birth, a child knows nothing about speech. It has never made a sound. It is anatomically incapable of doing much more than cry, because it cannot breathe through its mouth. If you hold a baby's nose, it suffocates. It is, at first, an obligatory nose-breather but, about three months after birth, things change. The jaw pulls forward and the nerves are re-programmed to operate a new and more complex pattern of breathing. This transitional period is a dangerous one. It coincides with the peak of mysterious Sudden Infant Death Syndrome, which kills a distressing number of apparently perfectly healthy babies. Both, however, stop at an age of five or six months, when we are free for the first time to breathe either through nose or mouth, by choice, as the larynx drops into its accustomed human place.

The larynx itself is a bit of a mystery. It is essentially a tubular structure at the upper end of the windpipe which, in most mammals, connects directly with the back of the nasal passages. The object is to provide a channel from the nostrils to the lungs that remains open all the time, so that animals can breathe and swallow simultaneously. However, in humans the larynx makes a strange move, one that kills babies and goes on threatening our lives. It shifts to an awkward position low down in the throat, right in the path of all food and drink on its way to the gullet. So, every time we swallow, the larynx has to move upwards again and shelter beneath the base of the tongue, hiding from incoming solids and liquids. You can see this readjustment taking place by the bobbing of the 'Adam's apple', the thyroid cartilege attached to the larynx, in every diner's throat.

Most of the time, the manoeuvre works well. Every now and then, however, something goes down the wrong way and we choke and have to be rescued, if we are lucky, by a waiter or friend who happens to know the antidotal Heimlich Manoeuvre for dislodging such an obstruction. There are risks too in the passage of solids and liquids that sometimes come back up the throat. Only humans drown in their own vomit. No other species is faced with such indignities. So there must be good evolutionary reasons for taking these chances. There are. The risks, it seems, are the price we pay for speech.

A lowered larynx not only gives us the option of breathing through our mouths. It also provides us with what one neurologist has called 'the oldest musical instrument, rich in harmonic content, of wide tonal compass, eminently portable, and completely idiosyncratic in performance, being played by its owner alone'. Our voice.

The human larynx is five centimetres high with a wedge-shaped opening. Two sides of this opening are lined with flat reed-like membranes, seventeen millimetres long in men and twelve millimetres in women, which interrupt the airflow from the lungs, producing sound. The pitch of this sound depends on the length of the membranes, making women's and children's voices naturally higher than those of adult men. Loudness depends on air pressure, with a shout building up as much as one-tenth of an atmosphere, while quality and control are largely a matter of training and practice.

A baby's larynx is just five millimetres wide and at first functions only as a valve, making it possible to shriek, cry or coo. The louder sounds are signals of hunger or discomfort, but cooing is a more subtle form of communication. Mothers and young infants spend a lot of time cooing at each other, practising imitation and building up a strong social bond. Then, at about eight weeks, the child takes off on its own and begins to babble. All human children do this and in exactly the same way, producing a liquid and wordless sound, a kind of gibberish that is quite independent of whatever language is being used by the parents. This babble is universal and represents a sort of 'first language', something common to our species, but not yet speech. Then the larynx descends and everything changes. The child gets its true voice and, sometime between six months and one-year-old, it suddenly stops babbling. It seems to pause to think about things and becomes quiet for a while. And then, as if it realises all at once what speech is about, begins to imitate adult sounds and sets about learning the 'second language', its home tongue. It is possible that this stage in our individual development reflects what happened in the history of our species.

The mystery of the descending larynx has been explained by suggestions that it was simply an accident of evolution. Something that happened when our faces flattened, forcing the back of the tongue down our throats; or was an inevitable consequence of the new way we held our heads when we first began to walk upright. However, there is another, more convincing, possibility.

There is one habitat in which a permanently open channel from nostrils to lungs ceases to be an asset. Water. You can't swallow food underwater unless you can isolate the nasal passages, and this can't be done with a larynx in the way. At least not if you are human and need to block the nose off with the soft palate. To do that, the larynx must descend, but once it does, you also gain control over respiration. Breathing becomes voluntary. Something you can do in the air and stop doing underwater. A trick known only to the diving animals, to seals and whales – and to man. This fact, together with features such as hairlessness and layers of subcutaneous fat, leads some anthropologists to believe that, several million years ago, we passed through an aquatic phase. If it is true that we were once aquatic apes, then this could be precisely the stimulus we needed to leave us, back on land again, with a new larynx and the kind of breath control necessary for playing it properly.

It is interesting that newborn babies swim like fish, and only later, at an age of about one year, start to talk. But once started, the process is extraordinarily rapid. At one, a child knows nothing of speech. At two, it knits words into simple sentences. At three, it talks incessantly. At four, most normal children have mastered the complex and abstract structure of even such difficult languages as English or Japanese. The problem with this is that three years is simply not enough time to do this by rote or simple learning.

It is clear that, once they begin, children possess a fierce drive to acquire speech, imitating sounds, making sense of them and then making use of them. Like good neophils, they glory in everything novel, inventing words, experimenting with meaning, creating new constructions and picking up the vital rules – all in sequence. It is something that comes on us like a fever. We seem, as a species, to have an innate capacity for stringing words together in certain ways, a sort of 'deep grammar' that makes the rapid acquisition of language possible. How else can one account for the fact that each of us, without a phrase book, with no concept of speech and no preconceived ideas about it, succeeds even before we go to school in bringing off such a stunning achievement?

It is almost as if, when we begin to speak, we learn what it is that we know.

20 仲間意識の中身

TWENTY

FELLOW FEELING

The great English biochemist J. B. S. Haldane was a selfless man. Someone who continually put himself at risk for the benefit of others. He was a true altruist, so there was some consternation when, in an interview near the end of his life in exile in India, he was asked if he would lay down his life for his brother, and he answered, 'No'. However, after a moment's thought, the geneticist in him added, 'I would do it for three brothers. Or, failing that, nine cousins.'

The mathematics are simple. A brother shares half your genes and a cousin one-eighth. If two of your brothers are drowning and you rescue them, but die yourself, the genetic equation is balanced. Nothing is gained. But if your brave act succeeds in saving three brothers, there is profit in the transaction. Fifty per cent more of yourself survives than if you had simply stood on the beach and done nothing. Blood, as the saying goes, is thicker than water, and the genes in blood are shrewd cost-accountants, keeping a sharp eye on the balance sheet. Self-sacrifice makes chemical sense in certain circumstances. But is that all there is to it? Must all grand gestures be reduced to this depressing arithmetic? Is there nothing more noble and interesting going on?

There is certainly something in us that counts the cost, recognising the benefits of helping those to whom we are related. Nepotism, the demonstration of favouritism toward relatives, is deeply rooted in biology. It is a universal human trait. Successful men everywhere find nice jobs for their nephews and, left only to the selfish devices of the genes, we all tend to hand out harsher treatment to those to whom we are less closely related. Sometimes me against my brother; more often me and my brother against our cousins; very often me and my brother and our cousins against the rest of the village; but usually all of us in the village against anyone else from outside.

When a stranger arrived at an Aboriginal camp in Australia, it was customary to keep him waiting outside, hot and nervous in the sun, until an old man, someone familiar with all the genealogies, could come out to interrogate him. If the stranger was found to be related, even distantly, to anyone in the camp, he was accepted. If not, he was killed.

The old poet's question, 'How do I love thee?' has a new biological response: 'Let me count the genes.' Robert Browning may disapprove, but this is very often the kind of calculation we make. In the United States, the highest award for bravery in peacetime is the Carnegie Medal, and the committee which decides on the award of this special honour takes care never to give it in recognition of valour shown in saving the life of a relative. That is expected. What is unexpected, and therefore considered worthy of a medal, is risking your life to help a stranger in distress. Which does happen, of course. Carnegie Medals are awarded every year, in contradiction of genetics. Why does this happen? What is it that sends total strangers to their death in heavy seas – not only in vain attempts to rescue an unfamiliar child, but sometimes even in aid of someone else's dog?

No one in such a situation expects to die, but it helps to understand the response if we look at the origins of suicide.

Some bacteria that are found in the human gut carry part of their inheritance in plasmids, free-floating little packets that live like viruses in the bacterial cell. One of these plasmids carries just two genes, and holds these in precarious balance. One gene is active most of the time, making an antidote to a particular poison. The other produces the poison. It does so, however, only when there is overcrowding – when too many bacteria exist in the gut, putting themselves and their host at risk. Then the antidote gene switches off, the poison gene turns on and the bacterium and all its contents die. The plasmid commits suicide. However, as the cell dies, poison is released into the whole gut, where it destroys all those bacteria which do not carry such plasmids. So, by giving up its own life, the plasmid ensures the survival of other plasmids like it. There is profit in the transaction. It makes evolutionary sense.

Cells in our bodies behave in a similar way. Many are programmed to commit suicide on cue. That's how we grow, how we protect ourselves from the harsh world outside, and how much of our physiology works. Ovulation, for instance, is inhibited in a nursing mother. Her eggs' cells die, giving up their destinies, practising a kind of pre-emptive abortion, enhancing the chances of related cells in the child still suckling. In some species, mothers wipe out all their cells, literally killing themselves in order to give their offspring a better headstart. Octopus even have a gene for dropping dead. This self-destruct device lies in the optic gland from where it orders the octopus to stop feeding as soon as she has laid her eggs. It keeps her on guard over the brood until these are old enough to look after themselves, whereupon she dies. Salmon practise the same kind of kamikaze parenthood, beating themselves to death in an exhausting journey upstream to spawn.

Humans, however, are not subject to the same restrictions. We live long enough to breed many times and seem to be unique in that, in addition to nurturing and caring for our own offspring, we are prepared to adopt, succour and make sacrifices for others with whom we share no genes at all. This is where we and the plasmids part company. They are completely tied to purely chemical threads which run vertically from one generation to the next, linking lines that share the same genes. Part of our behaviour is certainly based on the same principle – on blood ties that dictate loyalties and identify friends and enemies. However, we practise also a new and more sympathetic kind of horizontal association.

The pastoral people of East Africa, for instance, have a fearsome reputation amongst their neighbours. They are seen to be warlike. Anthropologists, however, can find no evidence in them of unusual aggression. They seem, on the contrary, to be very well adjusted, but what Masai, Turkana and Samburu all have in common is a need for dedicated warriors, a sort of army that can be raised at short notice to defend their large and precious cattle herds. All these people have solved their problem in the same way. By linking men of the same generation into an 'age-set', a society of individuals who don't necessarily share any genes, but who owe each other loyalties based on shared ceremonies and rituals they took part in together.

We are wonderfully inventive when it comes to making such associations, which need have nothing to do with waging war. We seem to have, in addition to our tendency to favour kith and kin, an inherent fondness for creating other alliances and ties, dedicating large parts of our life and energy to clans, clubs and societies. To scout troops, fan groups, craft guilds, street gangs and political parties. All are totally artificial, having no biological origins or genetic bonds. They are held together instead by names, symbols, mascots, flags and patriotic songs, but are not without social relevance. They are important to our mental health. They forge new allegiances. They lead, through natural and arranged marriages, to genetic connections in another generation. And they tell us something important about ourselves.

It seems likely that the explosive growth of our brains occurred because they were stretched to deal with the demands of living in larger and more mixed social groups. It was in these associations that we first learned the value and importance of generosity. It was reciprocal altruism within such societies that provided the cement that helped them grow, often against the selfish concerns of the genes.

Now it seems inevitable that, if our even more complex global culture is to survive, it will have to draw on reserves of selflessness we have not yet learned to tap. Our breadth of interest, our curiosity, our spirit of adventure, and our willingness to be inventive, to fly in the face of traditional genetic arithmetic, are all about to be tested to the limit.

It is a good thing we are neophilic.

21

意識の彼方へ

TWENTY-ONE

OUT OF MIND

Each of us has one, but knows nothing about it.

The human brain is, at the same time, our greatest asset and our deepest mystery. Despite 2,000 years of thinking with it, about it, we still don't begin to understand how it works. The problem has been neatly summarised in the observation that 'If the brain was so simple that we could understand it, we would be so simple that we couldn't.'

The Greek physician Galen recognised the brain as the seat of thought and the soul. He believed, however, that it was essentially a gland and that fluids from it pulsed down the pathways of the nerves to where the mind was actually housed. The discovery of brain-waves earlier this century led to descriptions of a more electrical nature, and a tendency to see the brain in terms of hardware. One neurologist still describes it as 'the most sophisticated and complicated machine that we are ever likely to encounter'.

The brain does indeed store our memories and perform all of the complex computations that govern our behaviour, giving us an integrated picture of the world. Its million million nerve cells and their millions of billions of connections, do invite comparison with computer circuits, but the design and architecture of the brain are very different. Thus a few scientists have begun to return to Galen's position, seeing the brain as software, as the centre of hormonal and chemical control. They are suggesting that real mindfulness could possibly take place elsewhere.

There do seem to be limits to purely electrical investigation of the brain. Despite the work of tens of thousands of people in hundreds of laboratories during the last fifty years, we still know nothing about the actual mechanisms of reasoning and remembering. We have identified electrical phenomena which accompany changes and abnormalities in the brain, but the waves themselves remain a mystery. We spend a third of our lives in radically altered states of brain activity known as sleeping and dreaming, but we still don't know how and why we do so. Or how we become aware while awake of anything at all.

As a biologist, I can see that simple awareness exists even amongst bacteria, which seem to be able to recognise self from others. However, there is a natural divide at the upper end of the evolutionary tree. We, and possibly apes and whales and a few other more complex creatures, have acquired the sort of self-awareness that comes with being conscious. Our nature has become relatively independent of our substance. We have been put together in ways that transcend our ingredients and give us new and startling talents. We have, somewhere along the line, picked up a magic ingredient which leads to the appearance of personality and the existence of mind.

I am, therefore I think.

Having started to think, having had the time to practise creativity we alone, at the spearhead of evolution, seem to have gone one huge step further. We have, somehow, even without knowing how it works, gained access to inspiration. Access to that state of consciousness in which we see things very clearly and frequently accomplish the impossible.

The condition can be largely physical. Racing drivers recognise a level of performance which exists beyond normal bounds. When danger suddenly threatens at 300 kilometres an hour, they can sometimes switch into personal overdrive and produce unusually brilliant manoeuvres. Taking action in split seconds, during which it feels to them as though they have all the time in the world. Tennis players, at their peak, describe a state in which they see the balls as several times their true size. Rock climbers become so absorbed, feeling at one with the cliff face, that they know instinctively where every handhold can be found. During his miracle leap in Mexico in 1968, when he broke the world long jump record by 58 centimetres, Bob Beamon felt that he existed for a moment outside himself, between time and space. Beamon's description of this condition sounds very much like the trance state in which chess masters usually play.

Such powerful concentration is rare, but something like it could be part of our everyday life. At the University of Chicago, psychologists have been looking at something they call 'the flow'. Mihaly Csikszentmihalyi and his colleagues have been studying athletes, artists and surgeons – people whose work requires a tight focus – and discovering that all know moments of complete clarity, when time is distorted and they have a sense of absolute mastery. The climber cannot conceive of falling, the surgeon cuts with certainty and the painter knows precisely where to lay his brush. They lose our normal sense of self, in which we are both actors and observers, and flow along with the task. While this is happening, there is a marked *decrease* of activity in the brain. It becomes electrically quiet, as though the party has moved on.

Csikszentmihalyi suggests that the flow is not confined to exceptional people. It takes place in everyone, as often as several times a day, but only when the task at hand is perfectly matched to the skill of the individual. Any other combination is counterproductive. When you meet a challenge that is greater than your skills, that's anxiety. When your skills exceed the challenge, that's boredom.

The beauty of this simple notion is that it begins to make sense of some of our strange preoccupations, many of which are impossible to understand in terms of either instinct or learning. High-risk activities like climbing and racing, and all the other mental and physical problems we place in our paths, fail to make sense in evolutionary terms. They have no survival value. But they do give us the chance to flow. The chess master who plays blindfolded against an amateur performs better than if he were not so handicapped. He puts himself in the flow. And enjoys the pleasure of flowing for its own sake. The state is its own reward.

The Chicago team has not yet found a way of inducing pure flow, of willing oneself into it. However, the state seems to have a lot in common with some techniques of meditation in which adherents learn to 'stop the world'. Flowing, like meditating, requires *less* rather than more effort, and works best when distortions and distractions are effectively screened out. It involves an ability to ignore time and to live entirely in the present and outside the self. Which begins to sound like an accurate description of most young children's state of mind.

Children are in a state of constant excited discovery. They pick up new abilities every day and are eager to match their blossoming skills against new challenges. They are perfect neophils and, to judge from the state of euphoria, the detachment induced by make-believe and play, have flow states all the time. This may account for the fact that all the great intuitions, the insights which make sense of life and mathematics, have come to men with playful minds. To those who can entertain wild ideas without feeling the need to pass judgement on them.

Brain may be tied to its molecules, but mind goes with the flow, passing beyond what is known to the source of inspiration. Wherever that might be.

22

芸術衝動

TWENTY-TWO

THE ARTISTIC IMPULSE

I have, on my wall, a painting by one of the most famous artists of our time. He lived in London where, during a few hectic years, he produced nearly 400 works. Most of these are abstract, line drawings and watercolours, which bear his distinctive signature – a fan shape near the centre of the composition. An unusual feature of this artist's career is that he stopped painting when he was just five years old. But the most interesting thing about him is that he was a chimpanzee. His name was 'Congo', the Picasso of the ape world.

Congo lived in the London Zoo, where he was introduced to art by Desmond Morris – the author of *The Naked Ape*, who was then curator of mammals. I came to own an original Congo because I was at that time a student of animal behaviour at the Zoo.

Watching Congo at work, was fascinating. It was obvious that the drive to draw was strong and needed no reward or reinforcement. Once started, Congo became so engrossed in his painting that he preferred it even to being fed, and threw a temper tantrum when attempts were made to stop him. He received absolutely no training and was given no guidance or help other than access to the necessary equipment of paper, brushes, charcoal and poster paints. Then he would compose. He was clearly aware of the limits of design, seldom letting his lines run over the margins of a sheet. He showed clear colour preferences and a familiarity with the rudiments of composition, balancing forms, deliberately offsetting his efforts if there was something on the paper already. During the years he worked, Congo's style and his calligraphy changed, progressing along roughly the same path of development as that shown by very young children. Arriving, near the end of his career, at the state of diagrams, of circles and crosses, that immediately precede representational art.

Congo never did produce a self-portrait or a still life, but there is no question that he, and a total of twenty-two other chimpanzees, two gorillas, three orang-utans and four capuchin monkeys all demonstrated true artistic impulses and a grasp of the elements of aesthetics.

Nor are they alone in the animal world.

Amongst birds, the creative sense seems to be most strongly manifest in a group that live in Australasia. They are not particularly showy birds, few of them going in for the bright plumage that males of some species adopt to attract the attention of females during the breeding season. This group found such tactics too dangerous and discovered, somewhere along the line, that it was sexually just as effective to carry someone else's bright feather, as it was to grow one of your own. It was also a lot easier to get rid of the revealing advertisement when there were predators around. So, in the course of evolution, the males of these species came to look just as drab as their mates. However, they more than compensated for this discrepancy by collecting and displaying borrowed bits of plumage, and other bright banners, in and around a special mating area. They took to building and decorating honeymoon homes or bowers.

Bowerbirds have become the artists of the avian world. There are eighteen species of them and fourteen construct elaborate stick palaces or passageways of grass and twigs. Most stand on circular lawns which are carefully cultivated and decorated daily with a bewildering array of brightly-coloured feathers and berries, iridescent insect wings and fresh flowers. They tend these constructions assiduously, discarding and replacing the flowers when they fade, the fruit when it decays, often travelling great distances to collect appropriately coloured artefacts such as shotgun cartridges, bottle tops and cigarette lighters to add to their compositions.

There is nothing random about such collections. The satin bowerbird *Ptilonorynchus violaceus* in New South Wales has a distinct preference for blue objects, particularly the vivid wing feathers of one kind of parrot. If he cannot find enough of these in the vicinity of his bower, the satin bowerbird stoops to stealing them from his neighbours in order to enhance his own sex-appeal.

The gardener bowerbird *Amblyornis inornatus* in Papua is the dullest of all the species, but makes up for this by building the best bower – a massive tower, three metres high, of sticks woven and glued together with resin and saliva. This stands in a moss garden and is decorated with shells, stones, nuts and leaves, all painted glossy black with a pigment made from a mixture of charcoal, crushed berries and oily excrement, and applied quite deliberately to the bower with a paintbrush of fibrous plant material.

The results are beyond dispute. The bowerbirds build and decorate the most refined objects in the animal kingdom. They do so, and continue to do so, because it works. The bowers attract females and enhance their reproductive success. Nevertheless, it would be wrong to concentrate only on the functional and adaptive aspects of such behaviour. The bowers are far more beautiful than they need to be. The results are so clearly aesthetic, even to our eyes, that it is difficult not to feel that some real awareness exists. The necessary effects are often achieved by careful, and apparently considered, selection and placement of a particular berry or a splash of paint, when any bright object placed almost anywhere would have served equally well, if the only purpose of the display was to attract the unthinking attention of a female.

Chimps and bowerbirds are both tool-users, skilled in making, adapting and using what they find around them to change their environment. A few of these techniques are inborn but, in chimps at least, some of them are passed on as traditions from one generation to the next, and all are improved with practice. There is room in the process for invention and exploration, for individuals to gain new advantage by adding to and adapting their species behaviour patterns. There is survival value in the sort of improvisation that led to the origin of art. But also something more.

The same reasoning applies to human endeavours. We spent ninety-nine per cent of our history as hunters, during all of which time we made our own tools. The shape of a tool and skill in its construction were important for survival. Success in making them paid off. Up to a point. But, like the bowerbirds, we went past that point and began to make things that were unnecessarily beautiful.

The handaxe is a case in point. Starting about a million years ago, it became the Boy Scout knife of the ancient world. It was clearly widely used, but remains mysterious. The delicacy and symmetry of its design, the quality of the workmanship involved, and the time devoted to its manufacture, all went far beyond functional demand. A cruder instrument, much more simply made, would have been just as effective. However, like the chimp with his painting and the bird with his bower, we seem to have found satisfaction in the creation of something lovely for its own sake.

The handaxe was perhaps our first essay in style, but it was not our last. The painting of bodies and cave walls followed, and developed, through representation, to art as a vital part of magic and ritual. The process went on, later still, to the use of art in the development of culture and mental capacity in the form of records and writing. However, it seems certain that none of this would have happened if we had not, in the first place, been fascinated – as young chimps still are – by the pleasure of creation.

It is nice that we are one of those inventive species with a fondness for things that are new, but it is even better to know that we have a talent for selecting, from all that is merely novel, those bits that also have aesthetic merit.

23
心の調べ

TWENTY-THREE

FACING THE MUSIC

In the days before steam, it was possible to hear everything that happened on a ship. To listen to the timbers talking and hear the complaint of ropes under tension in the wind. These sounds were familiar to sailors, who noticed them only when they stopped. But there were other calls in the night which were less familiar and which led to a belief in haunted ships and the dreaded siren's song.

The constant clatter of powered vessels obscured the sounds and the fears for a while, but both reappeared during World War II when hydrophones were first used in an attempt to track down enemy submarines. Those manning such listening posts on both sides soon learned to recognise natural sea sounds such as croaking fish, snapping shrimp or the crash of surf on a distant shore. However, there were other sounds so unexpected in character that the listeners found it hard to believe these were not evidence of some diabolical new weapon.

By 1951, SOFAR (Sound Fixing and Ranging) stations had been set up around the world and were reporting the same strange noises in oceans everywhere. There were low-frequency moans, a series of thumps so regular that they became known to analysts as 'the A-train', and a peculiar 'boing' sound precisely four seconds long. The mystery was only solved when, by chance, recordings were played to an old sailor who had gone to the Antarctic fishing grounds in a

wooden ship. He unhesitatingly identified the sounds as the
voices of fin, piked and blue whales, describing how he and all
the old-time whalers had tracked their quarry down by such
characteristic calls.

We now know that all cetaceans are highly vocal and that one,
at least, is a virtuoso performer. Humpback whales, *Megaptera
novaeangliae*, produce an astonishing range of grunts, moans,
moos, rasps, twitters and whistles that have been found, on
analysis, to be arranged into an organised sequence that can only
be described as a song. The form is an appealing one, even to a
human ear. It is made up of short sound units combined into
phrases which form unbroken patterns or themes. These recognisable themes are subject to individual interpretation, but all are
arranged into cycles characteristic of a particular population.
Such structures give whales in Bermuda or Hawaii their own
local dialects, but provide the species everywhere with traditional songs that run from six to thirty minutes long, and are
often performed in ritual collections or concerts that go on, without repetition, for over twenty-four hours.

These performances have been compared, for complexity,
with the entire series of Wagner's *Der Ring des Nibelungen*
operas. However, no single human singer could sustain a solo
of such length or intricacy, or hope to match the whale's range,
which soars from deep bass groans to supersonic soprano
squeaks. The humpback's song is now, justifiably, recognised
as the most elaborate single display in the animal kingdom.

There are others.

The European blackbird *Turdus merula* has a complex song
sequence. When a blackbird is singing well, by which I mean
singing in a way which appeals aesthetically to our ears, it
seems to be exploiting this repertoire to the full. Such singing
is basically a territorial display, it warns rival males to stay
away. When one does approach, a resident bird sings more
energetically, but he doesn't necessarily become more musical.
On the contrary, he seems to get upset and his song tends to
grow disjointed, with long pauses and unfinished phrases. It is
only later in the season, when he no longer has to worry about
attracting mates or repelling intruders, that a blackbird relaxes

and sings well, by his or our standards. His performances then become more elaborate and more organised, in a manner so closely resembling our own ideas of musical form that it is difficult to deny that they are aesthetically improved.

In Africa, boubou shrikes, *Laniarius aethiopicus*, have turned their species' song into elaborate duets. These colourful birds live in thick bush where mated pairs keep contact with each other by means of wonderful fluted calls. A single sound would serve equally well, but each boubou produces a liquid sequence of notes that elicits an instant and antiphonal response from its mate. The reply is a variation, in pitch and tone, of the first call, but follows so directly that the exchange sounds like a single song. It is also a very flexible song, because the pair keeps improvising, working out new and distinctive combinations, each more musical than the last.

It is hard not to interpret such performances in musical terms. They are more elaborate than signals need to be, and sound more like celebration than simple communication. There is, indeed, a chimpanzee display that is even called a 'carnival'. It is said to keep a colony of apes in contact in dense rainforest, or to draw a troop together at a good feeding site. However, as a signal, it has to be considered excessive. The whole group shout and howl, they shake branches, clap their hands, leap up and down, and drum rhythmically with their feet on the resonant buttresses or trunks of trees. The result is a controlled sort of pandemonium, not unlike the hullabaloo of a human carnival, in which loud song and dance serves to draw people together, to direct the emotions of such a group, and to prepare it for joint action later.

Human music has moved on from simple signals in the same way that human language has been liberated from the rituals of much animal communication. Both now have their own syntax. Our response to music clearly has very deep roots. Roughly half of the languages in the world are tonal in character, and all make wide use of musical intonations. It is significant that brain-damaged individuals, who are completely incapable of normal speech, are often still able to sing, even without tuition.

A basic musical ability seems to be built in to our bodies. It is one of the characteristics of our species. The music is in us, as it is in shrikes and whales and chimpanzees, and it will find a way out. However, the way in which it is expressed depends on our societies. Music is organised sound and the patterns of its organisation are culturally determined. It is a way of sharing experience, so the difference between music in one society and another tends to be social rather than musical.

If European music seems more complex than African music and is practised by smaller groups of people, it is because of the division of labour in each society, and not because Europeans are less rhythmic or their music necessarily more evolved. It is different, but it follows the same rules. Composition in either society may appear to be the result of efforts by gifted and exceptional individuals, but it is better described as a collective effort that is expressed in the behaviour of certain individuals. In every case it tells us something about the conditions in which it was created. It carries information about mood and mental set as clearly and as precisely as the song of a blackbird identifies its species and physiological condition.

A Beethoven symphony, a Cantonese opera, an African folk song, or a piece designed to be played by Indian sitar, Japanese koto or Balinese gamelan are technically distinct. However, all are expressions of consciousness, of our need to say something new and important about the way we feel. The best of such music leaps across cultural and even species boundaries, giving inventive neophilic creatures an extraordinary reach.

There is comfort of a sort to be found in the results of a recent experiment in which rats were raised to the accompaniment of either Mozart or Stockhausen, and showed a unanimous preference for classical harmonies, many apparently becoming deeply moved by the 40th Symphony.

24

リアリティの本質

TWENTY-FOUR

THE NATURE OF REALITY

Why don't animals have wheels?

A silly question? Perhaps. It's not the sort of thing that most biologists worry about, but it is worth considering. Why don't they? The simple answer might be that nature never provided any roads for them to run on, but this is not really true. Most of the world land speed records have been set on salt pans and lake beds that are flatter, wider and truer than any highway ever made by man.

A more considered answer would be one that takes into account the fact that no organism has ever evolved so much as a gear or a cog, let alone a fully functional wheel. This leads to the conclusion that life evolved within the constraints set by the laws of physics and geometry.

There is a lot of truth in this.

The cube/square law, for instance, holds that an object which doubles its height and width, cubes its volume. This means that elephants are effectively limited to a maximum height of about four metres. An eight metre elephant would weigh around 40,000 kilograms and have to support a mass equivalent to that of a normal adult elephant resting on each of its four legs. It would never be able to stand up at all.

The fossil record shows that nature has experimented with a wide variety of animal shapes, and reveals that it keeps coming up with the same arrangements. The two-part hinged shell characteristic of clams, for example, has appeared at least eight times amongst molluscs, insects and crustaceans. Furthermore, eyes remarkably like our own have evolved independently as many as forty times in different groups of organisms.

The nature of embryological growth, where things split in half again and again, means that we get an occasional two-headed monster. But nobody is ever likely to see anything like the three-headed giants so popular in fairy tales. There are limits to what can happen. In fact, most things that can happen, have already done so. If there is life anywhere else in the universe, the chances are that it will look rather familiar. And it won't have wheels.

Evolution everywhere obeys the same basic laws. Or at least it did so until we came along. Now, it seems, things may have changed. Simply because we are here.

The structure of the universe is determined by a few simple laws that govern how bodies move about. Newton described these 300 years ago, and for most situations his mechanics are still adequate, only failing when the bodies involved are very small. Under these circumstances we have to resort to a new system of mechanics based on the behaviour of submicroscopic units called quanta.

Quantum theory suggests, amongst other things, that particles can and do influence each other at a distance by the exchange of messengers such as photons. Communication of this sort at a basic level produces the whole catalogue of extraordinary coincidences which are known to exist.

The same physical arrangements keep cropping up again and again in different contexts, as if the supply of suitable patterns was very limited. Heat, light, sound, magnetism, electricity and even gravity operate in accordance with a surprisingly small number of universal constants – and they seem to do so everywhere. The number of stars in a typical galaxy is the same as the number of galaxies in the universe. There is an astonishing similarity between the age of the universe and the number of particles in it. And so on. All of which leads physicists to believe that there must be a hidden principle at work, organising the cosmos in a coherent way. As there is no such principle apparent in fundamental physics, some scientists have turned to biology for an answer, and have come up with a surprising one.

Us.

Science used to exclude the human observer from its experiments. You have to be objective, it said. We don't matter. We are here just for the ride. But all that changed in 1927.

In 1927, the German physicist Werner Heisenberg drew attention to a problem. Suppose, he said, that you want to examine something. We can only see things by looking at them, which means bouncing photons of light off them. Since a photon is so small it doesn't do anything to disturb an elephant, even one of normal size and weight. Thus it is unlikely that an elephant going about its cumbersome business will become aware of our distant gaze. But an electron is different. It is so small itself that a single photon can knock it off orbit or even out of its atom altogether, so it is impossible to examine an electron in any detail. Electrons evade human examination not because we are too stupid or too clumsy, or lack the patience necessary to creep up on them unawares, but because it can't be done.

By observing anything, said Heisenberg, we change it. If you try to record the position of an electron, you change its momentum. If you attempt to measure its momentum, you change its position. We cannot, as a matter of principle, ever know the present in all its detail, simply because it is impossible not to be involved. There is no such thing as an objective experiment. Worse than that, there is no result to any experiment at all, unless an experimenter is there, observing what happens. And if we are there, we become inextricably involved. We play a part in deciding how the experiment comes out.

This may sound like a weird metaphysical notion, but it is in fact an accurate description of how things work. It is a description that makes sense in the terms of quantum mechanics, which has been found to be flawlessly successful at all levels of the world accessible to measurement. We do, it seems, drastically change the universe just by looking at it. We exist, and the fact of our existence constrains the structure of the cosmos, selecting what it must be like, pointing it in a certain direction. It is acceptance of this responsibility that has led to what is being called the Anthropic Principle. At first, this sounds ridiculous and egocentric. Yet another example of humans exaggerating their own importance. However, the scientists involved are the ones at the forefront of the new physics, and they are serious about it.

The astrophysicist Brandon Carter says, 'The universe must be such as to admit conscious beings in it at some stage.' This amounts to saying that it had no choice. Things have to be arranged, all the physical coincidences had to occur in order to put us on a solid surface near a stable star.

The nuclear mathematician John Barrow insists that, 'Our existence imposes a stringent selective effect upon the type of universe we could expect to observe.' In other words, we select precisely the conditions we need.

The theoretical physicist John Wheeler is quite positive about it. 'Here we are,' he says, 'so what must the universe be?' Wheeler suggests, in this simple statement that, by being here at all, we make it necessary to assume that things would be different if we were not.

None of these philosophical scientists is claiming that we create the universe. At least not in the usual sense of the word 'create'. They are not setting us up as gods. Nevertheless, they are all aware of the fact that the process of measurement in quantum physics *demands* the participation of a conscious observer at a fundamental level. They *are* suggesting that things, as we know them, are the inevitable consequence of our existence.

What good is a universe without awareness of it?

So perhaps animals don't have wheels simply because we couldn't imagine an elephant on axles. Maybe it is just as well that there are natural limits to our neophilia.

CONCLUSION

結び

CONCLUSION

We enjoy diversity.

Museums, aquariums, zoological and botanical gardens, collections of all kinds, fascinate us. They are amongst the most popular attractions in cities everywhere. The odder the exhibit, the more it differs from what we already know, the better we like it.

Yet we have come to take diversity for granted.

This is something quite new. A century ago, naturalists, anthropologists, archaeologists – enthusiasts of all kinds – scoured the world in search of variety, and found it everywhere, because diversity is the hallmark of flourishing life. It is an intrinsic feature of our natural world, in which biologists have already identified 1,700,000 different species of plants and animals. It was, however, a celebration of these very riches that brought about a change.

The process began with a twenty-eight-year-old Swedish botanist. In 1735, Carolus Linnaeus published *Systema Naturae*, a slim book of just seven pages, in which he established the first truly methodical way of describing and classifying living things. He exalted in diversity, revelling in every minute distinction, listing and recording everything he saw, so that by the tenth edition of his revolutionary work, it had grown to a colossal 2,500 pages.

Linnaeus brought order to the confusion of creation, making natural history systematic. And, by doing so, he changed the way we think. He was the first great generalist, showing how it was possible to assemble apparently unrelated information, odd animals, into larger and larger groups, demonstrating relationships, making sense of their similarities. He started a

train of thought which led inexorably to Charles Darwin and
the theory of evolution. And much more.

Linnaeus was directly responsible for creating a mindset that
has brought about an Age of Generality, the scientific and
technological era in which we now live. A time when diversity
has gone out of style. Taxonomy is old-fashioned. There is no
money or future in it. As a subject, it no longer attracts
the best brains. The discovery of DNA has underlined the
communality of things, and those few who persist in celebrating
diversity for its own sake are dismissed as mere collectors of
stamps.

This change in emphasis was useful, it brought considerable
rewards in understanding, but it has also begun to be very
dangerous. It puts us all at risk.

The problem is that we have come to look at diversity as
though it exists in an endless supply. We treat living species
as raw materials, as something expendable, as resources to
be used and removed unless they can be shown to have a
specific economic value. As a result, we are facing a global
crisis of extinction.

Plants have been evolving here for 4,000 million years. By
the latest count, there are 265,000 different species of them
around, but at least 25,000 of these are now threatened.
That is four times as many as Linnaeus listed in his *Species
Plantarum*. Before the end of this century, we can expect to
lose all 25,000 of these entirely.

Most plant species are tropical, flowering in the moist confusion of rainforests. However, one-third of such forests have
already been cut down, and we are losing another 200,000
square kilometres every year. If this rate of clearance continues, all undisturbed forest will disappear in the next thirty
years, and with it, not just 160,000 kinds of plants, but at least
a million known species of animals. And perhaps another 30
million species that have not yet been, and never will be,
described.

Economists of the Age of Generality say that such destruc-
tion doesn't matter. They claim that the value of these species
has been greatly exaggerated, and that we have good substi-

tutes for them anyway. Their estimates of cost and benefit lead to conclusions which suggest that the Amazon, for instance, will be 'improved' when its 90,000 native plant species are traded in for three or four introduced trees that are known to be useful to man. This staggering conceit completely ignores the fact that tropical soils are notoriously poor, and that monocultures there are equally notoriously vulnerable to fire and disease. Such an approach does not even begin to address the problems already raised by loss of diversity in domesticated crops and livestock. We may have developed novel techniques of genetic engineering, but we are rapidly losing the material on which to put such tools to work. Since 1970, almost 1,000 independent seed companies in the West have been bought out by inter-national corporations, who now only stock a few hundred of the 6,000 fruit and vegetable varieties that were once on sale.

Modern market practices make it almost impossible for farmers to grow or sell anything but a few common kinds of fruit – the usual apples, peaches and pears. Supermarkets like things to be standardised. In Europe alone, fifty-one breeds of horse, eighty-one breeds of cattle and sixty-seven breeds of sheep, are now officially listed as endangered. A priceless heirloom will soon be lost forever, and without the gene bank of the tropical forests, there will be no possibility of replacing it. Not in less than the four or five billion years it took to grow.

These frightening consequences are only part of a more general malaise. We have gone so far along the road to genera-lity that we seem unable any longer to look around us and see what is happening. The world is in a mess. And it continues to slide ever deeper into chaos while the high-priests of tech-nology go on creating fantasy worlds, preaching the gospel of industrial paradise.

By the year 2000, they say, we will have solved most of our problems. Water shortages will be a thing of the past, thanks to icebergs towed up from the Antarctic. There will be pills for almost everything and drugs to make our hair grow and keep our teeth free of cavities. We will be immunised from birth against tuberculosis, cancer and AIDS. We will live longer, some of us with artificial livers and spleens. Cars will be owned by everyone and be half the present weight, getting twice the mileage. Computers will control a cashless society and science will be free to solve some of the riddles of the universe from manned space stations.

Quite possibly. The opportunism and curiosity of our species remains enormous. For nations such as the United States, Australia and China, with their wealth of raw materials, this vision may come true. But for most of the world population, it's just not going to be like that. Not unless we can balance our technical prowess with a willingness to be equally inventive on the social front. It seems to me that this can only be accomplished if we can succeed in resisting the blandishments of perpetual economic growth and establish the cultural equivalent of a gene bank.

We need to cherish and preserve human diversity. We must learn to respect and protect the rich body of tradition that still exists, and use it to feed our hunger for novelty and, at the same time, nourish our planet.

Neophilia, the tradition of the new, grows from old and well-established roots. It needs to be earthed.

BIBLIOGRAPHY

INTRODUCTION

MORRIS, D. *The Human Zoo*. London: Jonathan Cape, 1969.

1 IN THE BEGINNING

GRIBBIN, J. *In Search of the Big Bang*. London: Heinemann, 1986.
HAWKING, S. W. 'Breakdown of predictability in gravitational collapse', *Physics Review* D14: 2460, 1976.
WEINBERG, S. *The First Three Minutes*. London: Deutsch, 1977.

2 THE WHOLE EARTH

LOVELOCK, J. *Gaia*. Oxford University Press, 1979.
RUSSELL, P. *The Awakening Earth*. London: Routledge & Kegan Paul, 1982.
STAPLEDON, O. *Starmaker*. Harmondsworth: Penguin, 1972.

3 SIGNS OF LIFE

CAIRNS-SMITH, G. 'Signs of Life', *New Scientist*, 2 January 1986.
CAIRNS-SMITH, G. *The Life Puzzle*. University of Toronto Press, 1971.
DAVIES, P. C. W. *The Accidental Universe*. Cambridge University Press, 1982.

4 ORDER AND DISORDER

GARDNER, M. *Order and Surprise*. Oxford University Press, 1984.

5 BEING AND KNOWING

HUMPHREY, N. *The Inner Eye*. London: Faber & Faber, 1986.
PREMACK, D. & WOODRUFF, G. 'Does the chimpanzee have a theory of mind?' *Behavioral and Brain Sciences 4* : 515, 1978.

6 ONE MAN'S MEAT

WILSON, E. O. *On Human Nature*. Harvard University Press, 1978.

7 THE TROUBLE WITH SEX

CHERFAS, J. & GRIBBIN, J. *The Redundant Male*. London: The Bodley Head, 1984.
HAMILTON, W. D. 'Sex versus non-sex versus parasite', *Oikos 35* : 282, 1980.

8 MAKING SENSE

HUXLEY, A. *The Doors of Perception*. London: Chatto & Windus, 1954.
JOHNSON, R. *The Imprisoned Splendour*. New York: Harper & Row, 1953.

9 SEEING IS BELIEVING

CARPENTER, E. *Oh, What a Blow that Phantom Gave me!* New York: Holt, Rinehart & Winston, 1973.

10 NOW HEAR THIS

BIRNHOLZ, J. C. & BENACERRAF, B. R. 'The development of human fetal hearing', *Science 222* : 516, 1983.
SMITH, A. *The Mind*. London: Hodder & Stoughton, 1984.
ZUCCARELLI, H. 'Ears hear by making sounds', *New Scientist*, 10 November 1983.

11 SOUND EFFECTS

ROBINS, D. 'The Dragon Project and the talking stones', *New Scientist*, 21 October 1982.
SOBEL, D. 'Infrasonic elephants', *Omni*, September 1986.

12 SMELLING GOOD

DOTY, R.L. 'Communication of gender from human breath odors', *Hormones and Behaviour 16* : 13, 1982.
McCLINTOCK, M. K. 'Menstrual synchrony and suppression', *Nature 229* : 244, 1971.
PORTER, R. H. & MOORE, J. D. 'Human kin recognition by olfactory cues', *Physiology and Behaviour 27* : 493, 1981.

13 SENSES OF DIRECTION

BECKER, R. O. & SELDEN, G. *The Body Electric*. New York: Morrow, 1985.
TROMP, S. W. *Biometeorology*. London: Heyden, 1980.
WILLIAMSON, S. et al. (eds.) *Biomagnetism*. New York: Plenum, 1983.

14 EXTRASENSORY PERCEPTION

RHINE, J. B. & FEATHER, S. R. 'The study of cases of "psi-trailing" in animals', *Journal of Parapsychology 26* : 1, 1962.
STEVENSON, I. 'Telepathic impressions', *Journal of the American Society for Psychical Research 29* : 1, 1970.
TARG, R. & PUTHOFF, H. 'Information transmission under conditions of sensory shielding', *Nature 251* : 602, 1974.

15 CATCHING FIRE

CHERFAS, J. 'Cults play with fire', *New Scientist*, 20 June 1985.
DOHERTY, J. 'Hot feat', *Science Digest*, August 1982.
GOTTFRIED, B. S. et al. 'The Leidenfrost phenomenon', *International Journal of Heat and Mass Transfer 9* : 1167, 1966.

16   TAKING CONTROL

BROWN, B. D. *New Mind, New Body*. London: Hodder & Stoughton, 1974.

CADE, C. M. & COXHEAD, N. *The Awakened Mind*. Hounslow: Wildwood, 1974.

WALLACE, R. K. et al. 'A wakeful hypometabolic state', *American Journal of Physiology 221* : 795, 1971.

17   IN SEASON

EYSENCK, H. & NIAS, D. *Astrology*. London: Temple Smith, 1982.

GAUQUELIN, M. *The Truth About Astrology*, Oxford: Blackwell, 1983.

SMITHERS, A. 'The Zodiac Test', *The Guardian*, 19-23 March 1984.

18   FACE TO FACE

CALDER, N. *The Human Conspiracy*. London: BBC, 1976.

DARWIN, C. *The Expression of the Emotions in Man and Animals*. London: Murray, 1872.

FIELD, T. M. et al. 'Discrimination and imitation of facial expressions by neonates', *Science 218* : 179, 1982.

19   TALKING BACK

BROWN, R. *A First Language*. Harvard University Press, 1973.

MORGAN, E. & VERHAEGEN, M. 'In the beginning was the water', *New Scientist*, 6 March 1986.

SMITH, A. *The Body*. London: Penguin, 1986.

20   FELLOW FEELING

BARASH, D. *Sociobiology*. London: Souvenir, 1980.

MAYNARD SMITH, J. *The Problems of Biology*. Oxford University Press, 1986.

REYNOLDS, V. *The Biology of Human Action*. San Francisco: Freeman, 1976.

21   OUT OF MIND

BEGLEY, S. 'Going with the flow', *Newsweek*, 2 June 1986.
BERGLAND, R. *The Fabric of the Mind*. London: Viking, 1986.
BURNE, J. 'Half a mind to meditate', *New Scientist*, 21 August 1986.

22   THE ARTISTIC IMPULSE

GREIG-SMITH, P. 'Avian ideal homes', *New Scientist*, 2 January 1986.
MORRIS, D. *The Biology of Art*. New York: Knopf, 1962.
WASHBURN, S. L. 'A possible evolutionary basis for aesthetic appreciation in men and apes', *Evolution 24* : 824, 1970.

23   FACING THE MUSIC

BLACKING, J. *How Musical is Man?* London: Faber, 1976.
HINDE, R. A. *Bird Vocalisations*. Cambridge University Press, 1969.
PAYNE, R. & McVAY, S. 'Songs of humpback whales', *Science 173* : 585, 1971.

24   THE NATURE OF REALITY

BARROW, J. D. & TIPLER, F. J. *The Anthropic Principle*. Oxford University Press, 1982.
DAVIES, P. C. W. *The Accidental Universe*. Cambridge University Press, 1982.
WHEELER, J. A. *The Physicist's Conception of Nature*. Amsterdam: Reidel, 1978.

CONCLUSION

CETRON, M. & O'TOOLE, T. *Encounters with the Future.* New York: McGraw Hill, 1982.

EHRENFELD, D. 'Thirty million cheers for diversity', *New Scientist*, 12 June 1986.

LYALL WATSON

GIFTS OF UNKNOWN THINGS

Lyall Watson continues his fascinating investigation into so-called supernatural happenings. In his search for an understanding of other realities, Dr Watson became part of a small community living on a volcanic island in Indonesia, a community where extra-sensory perception, psychic healing, precognition, power places and survival after death are taken for granted.

In seeking explanations acceptable to the ever-changing theories of Western science, he describes an intriguing personal story which is a perfect blend of mystical happening and scientific investigation.

'It is, of course, completely different from the earlier books, but I found it equally absorbing. I found it one of the most fascinating things of its kind I have ever read'

Colin Wilson

'It is impossible not to be impressed and intrigued by his spectacular soundings in these strange waters'

The Observer

LYALL WATSON

LIFETIDE

Lyall Watson looks at recent developments in astronomy, biology and psychology, combining them with the experience of his own ten years' search into the mysterious.

A scientist himself, yet one who refuses to accept the traditional and self-imposed boundaries of science, he suggests that we are ourselves responsible for much that bemuses us, for phenomena such as ghosts, monsters and UFOs, for the supernatural and the extra-terrestrial.

In LIFETIDE, in the deep tidal flow of our unconscious, lie answers to the mysteries of dreams and visions, of precognition, reincarnation and human creativity itself.

'Lyall Watson has achieved a remarkable feat: he has managed to plait the diverse strands from his earlier books into a coherent philosophy – potentially a new biological paradigm'
Brian Inglis in The Guardian

LYALL WATSON

SUPERNATURE II

Thirteen years after SUPERNATURE stunned a generation, Lyall Watson breaks new ground along the frontiers of knowledge.

Science has put man on the moon, split the atom, reached the threshold of the secret of life itself. Yet it still can't explain how Uri Geller can bend a spoon, let alone how hundreds of youngsters can watch him do it on television and then do likewise . . . nor how an elderly Pole can run his hands over a small stone and produce an intimate, eye-witness account of life in the Magdelenian culture of 15,000 years ago . . .

Science can dismiss these and similar instances as charlatanism, hallucination or just plain nonsense, but Lyall Watson insists that the past decade and a half has produced more than enough evidence for the facts that will not fit . . .

'Dr Watson is not afraid to think the unthinkable: for instance that miracles might be actually quite common, but simply unnoticed most of the time. His openmindedness is refreshing'
Daily Telegraph

SUPERNATURE II was published in hardback under the title BEYOND SUPERNATURE.

sceptre

LYALL WATSON

HEAVEN'S BREATH

A unique and compelling study of the wind in all its guises.

From the dreaded 'ill winds' which drive men to murder and suicide, to the awesome 'winds of war' that determined the fate of the Spanish Armada, covering the history, physics and philosophy of this most vital natural force, *Heaven's Breath* is a treasure trove of information; thought provoking and consistently entertaining.

'A book which fascinates, delights and stimulates with a thousand fascinating facts'

Daily Mirror

'A comprehensive and fascinating study'
Bernard Levin's Book of the Year, The Observer, 1984

sceptre

LYALL WATSON

OMNIVORE
The Role of Food in Human Evolution

Why will we eat the same breakfast day after day, yet become outraged if the dinner menu doesn't change? Why do we never eat blue foods? Why are there topless waitresses but never topless usherettes? How are spinal disorders, ballistic missiles, and racial disturbances all linked to our diet?

These are just a few of the unprecedented questions answered in this lively, learned, and immensely informative exploration of the crucial role our eating habits have played in our evolution. Seasoned with wit, spiced with delicious insights into some of our more bizarre behaviour patterns, here is a revealing examination of how, through the ages, we have learned to play the eating game. OMNIVORE proves beyond all reasonable doubt that 'You are what you eat'.

OMNIVORE The Role of Food in Human Evolution was first published under the title THE OMNIVOROUS APE.